The World of the Woodchuck

LIVING WORLD BOOKS

John K. Terres, Editor

THE WORLD
OF THE
WOODCHUCK

Text and Photographs by

W. J. Schoonmaker

J. B. LIPPINCOTT COMPANY

PHILADELPHIA AND NEW YORK

To Jeannette, my wife

Contents

Author's Introduction

I believe that every one of us has been directly or indirectly influenced by those who have lived before. We may write because we were taught to write by teachers who were taught by other teachers. We may make photographs by using material and equipment that was discovered and perfected by others.

Although I have not known them, I am grateful to all of those who preceded me and left those precious somethings for all of us to enjoy and to use. And I am especially indebted to the scientists and naturalists who left written records of their observations and experiences so that I may better know and understand the woodchuck and the world in which it lives.

I am personally very grateful to my Editor, John K. Terres, who encouraged and helped me in many ways to undertake and complete this book. Also I give my thanks to my late friends and associates Dr. Charles C. Adams, Director of the New York State Museum, Dr. Homer D. House, New York State Botanist, Kenyon F. Chamberlain, Assistant New York State Entomologist, and especially to Dr. Sherman C. Bishop, New York State Zoologist, who was my Chief and very close friend.

W. J. SCHOONMAKER

Rensselaer, New York
February, 1966

Meet the Woodchuck

THE WOODCHUCK is a mammal because it is covered with hair, has mammary glands, and gives birth to living young that suckle on the breasts of the mother. Like other mammals it is warm-blooded, and like all other vertebrates it has a backbone. It never occurred to me, though, that the woodchuck is related to the squirrels, but it really does belong to the family Sciuridae. This family includes marmots, squirrels, and chipmunks; these animals vary in many ways. The chipmunk is small and has cheek pouches. Red and gray squirrels are expert tree climbers. The flying squirrel has a furry membrane joining its front and back legs so that it can glide through the air. Prairie dogs and ground squirrels are also members of this family, and the woodchuck, which in a sense is a ground squirrel, is the largest of all.

You may know the woodchuck by a different name, because it is also called ground hog, marmot, and just plain chuck. In the South it has still another name. Nearly forty years ago, in the mountains of North Carolina, I asked some men about the abundance of the woodchuck in the area. They did not seem to know the animal, but when I described it and told of its burrowing habits one man said, "Oh! You mean monax."

In 1743, Mark Catesby, writing about the natural history of Carolina, described the woodchuck under the name of monax, and this name was repeated in the writings of George Edwards in 1747. According to Ernest Thompson Seton, monax was an Indian name of the woodchuck and meant "the digger." It seems that Catesby and other early writers also learned about many of the animals from the Indians, and they knew them by their Indian names.

15

The family Sciuridae includes chipmunks, flying squirrels, and gray squirrels.

The World of the Woodchuck

The name marmot was brought from Europe. Woodchucks live in the old world as well as in North America; the alpine marmot, which lives in the Alps and Pyrenees, is but one example.

Our interest, however, is in North American animals. On this continent there are a number of kinds of woodchucks. They dwell from

The woodchuck is dark brown and has a short bushy tail.

New Mexico, Alabama, and Georgia north to Alaska, practically to the Arctic Circle. The woodchucks that I saw in North Carolina and those I saw in Canada looked about the same as the woodchucks I observed in the west in Montana and Wyoming. Within their range they vary somewhat in size and color, but their physical appearance is similar. Their way of life is also similar but may alter according to the locality in which each lives.

At a distance the woodchuck looks like a chunky, dark-brown animal with a short bushy tail. It is about the size of a cat and has legs so short that its belly seems to, and often does, scrape on the ground. A close-up

The yellow-bellied marmot weighs about seventeen pounds.

The white-footed mouse, another rodent, is related to the chuck.

view reveals that, although the color is generally brown, the back is grizzly gray and the feet and tail are very dark brown, almost black. You might say that it is bucktoothed because its front teeth protrude and can usually be seen at close range or with field glasses. These front teeth are not sharp and pointed for tearing flesh like the teeth of a cat; instead they are broad and chisel-shaped like those of a rabbit or squirrel. The woodchuck has therefore been classified as a rodent or gnawing mammal, and its teeth are perfectly suited for gnawing and

19

for eating grasses and other plants.

Like all other rodents, the chuck has no canine teeth, or fangs as they are sometimes called, but it does have grinding teeth. There are two premolars and three molars on each side of the upper jaw and one premolar and three molars on each side of the lower jaw. These plus

Incisors are visible at close range or through field glasses.

the four incisors add up to a total of twenty-two teeth. While the front teeth of some other rodents are orange, the incisors of the wood-chuck are white.

Woodchucks are the third largest North American rodent. The beaver, which has bright orange teeth, is the largest; I weighed one that was 65 pounds, and Vernon Bailey writes that there are records of 110-pound beavers. The porcupine, with brownish-orange incisors, will weigh up to about 35 pounds, so this animal is in second place. The western woodchuck, known as the yellow-bellied marmot, goes to about

17 pounds, and the hoary marmot, which lives in northwestern North America, may tip the scales at 20 pounds.

Mice are the smallest of the rodents, and there are a great many different kinds. Gerrit S. Miller, Jr., lists more than 140 varieties of the

The beaver is the largest North American rodent.

white-footed mouse alone, and this is but one of many species of mice. The pigmy mouse is the tiniest of all and weighs only about half an ounce, yet like the sixty-pound beaver it is distantly related to the woodchuck because it is a rodent.

One day while looking through my binoculars I saw the top of a chuck's head barely above the edge of its burrow. It was watching me, but without binoculars I would not have seen the animal. For the first time I became aware of the fact that the eyes, ears, and nose of the woodchuck are located very close to the top of its head so that the animal can see, hear, and smell with only its crown protruding above the rim of its burrow. To me this seemed to be very important because the den is the woodchuck's haven of safety, and the animal, in order to survive, must often see without being seen.

Since its home is underground, the woodchuck must be and is a powerful digger; its feet bear sturdy claws and its loose skin conceals short, thick leg bones and strong muscles.

Like the bear and raccoon and Man, also, the woodchuck is flat-footed, or plantigrade, and is not noted for its speed. I have chased them across open fields when I could run a hundred yards in ten seconds flat. Based upon a number of these races, I estimated the top speed of the creature at six to eight miles an hour.

Animals that walk on their toes can generally run faster than flat-footed animals. The red fox, which walks on its toes and weighs about the same as a woodchuck, may run at the rate of twenty-five miles an hour, but its legs are longer. However, all animals seem to be fitted for the life that they lead, and the woodchuck, secure in its burrow, has little need for speed.

A woodchuck peeks from its burrow.

Every female chuck that I examined had four pairs of teats, making a total of eight. However, Ernest Thompson Seton included a drawing of a female that had ten nipples, five on each side. William J. Hamilton, Jr., also noted this condition, reporting that he found extra pairs of teats in only two out of five hundred animals examined. In both, the accessary breasts were functioning.

I did not get an intimate view of the woodchuck until I attempted to shoot some close-ups with the camera. Working from a blind, I often took photos at fourteen feet, and when the wind was right the animals sometimes came to within a few feet of my camera. The way in which

The red fox, unlike the chuck, walks on its toes.

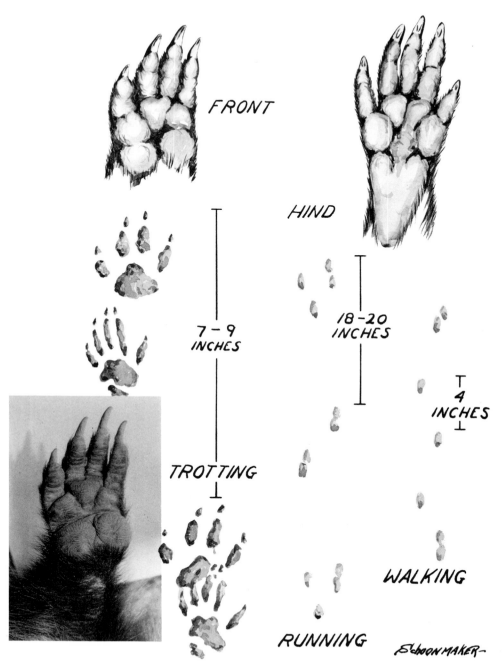

FRONT

HIND

7 – 9 INCHES

18 – 20 INCHES

4 INCHES

TROTTING

WALKING

RUNNING

Schoonmaker–

Drawings show the front and hind foot of the woodchuck and his tracks.

24

they used their front paws, which might be called hands, amazed me. They sat up on their haunches, clutched a stem of clover in one paw, and ate it as a boy does a banana. While they are not in the same class as the nimble-fingered raccoon, they are far more dexterous than the bear.

The hind foot of the ground hog has five well-developed toes and

The author's blind enabled him to take close-up photographs and make detailed observations.

measures about three to three and one-half inches in length. It has only four fingers, though, and the thumb on the forepaw is a mere knob. All fingers and toes bear claws.

I watched chucks walk and run over light snow and in this way learned to recognize their tracks. When the animal is walking, the

25

The grizzly bear cannot close its hand as do the raccoon and woodchuck.

imprint of the hind foot usually partly covers that of the front foot and the tracks are separated by about four inches. Trotting, the tracks are seven to nine inches apart. When the woodchuck is running its fastest, it gallops, and then the distance between the prints may be eighteen to twenty inches. The claws of both front and back feet show in the tracks.

Although the animal is flat-footed, the imprint of the full sole of the hind foot is seldom seen. However, the complete sole from toe to heel shows in the tracks of the raccoon and skunk, two other plantigrade mammals. The prints of these two are different from those of the woodchuck because each has five toes on the front foot. The track of the skunk is about the same size as that of the chuck, but the imprint of the hind foot of the skunk does not show claw marks. Also, when the skunk is running, its tracks are on a diagonal slant as though the animal were running on the bias. The raccoon is larger than the ground hog and so is its hind foot, which measures about four to five inches in length. The five toes that appear in the track are very long; one of my friends said that it reminded him of the imprint of a baby's foot.

The chuck uses its front paws like hands.

Many years ago I obtained a large woodchuck and carried it to my home, a distance of about four miles. I would have sworn that the animal weighed twenty pounds, but the scales recorded exactly half that weight. Since then I have heard hunters brag about big ones that weighed fully twenty-five pounds. However, no one has brought me such a giant, and the biggest woodchuck that I ever weighed was exactly thirteen pounds. This huge male, taken in late August when it was very fat, was twenty-six inches long, and that, too, was a record length.

27

I learned that woodchucks, like other animals, vary in weight according to their age and size and the season. (When I was young I weighed 135 pounds but now I weigh 170. I am the same height but thirty years older.) A young woodchuck will not weigh as much as an adult even though the total length of each is the same. Furthermore, a woodchuck will not weigh as much in late March as it will in September. The reason for this, I found, is that when the chuck emerges from hibernation in late winter the plants it eats have not yet begun to grow, and the animal is forced to exist on a starvation diet. It draws heavily from the fat stored in its body cavity and just under its skin. Because of this it loses weight; those that I weighed in late March and early April were about five to seven pounds. In July, after they have feasted on luscious clover and alfalfa, they are considerably heavier, and by late summer they have reached their peak. Fully grown animals that I recorded in the latter part of August weighed from nine to eleven or, rarely, twelve pounds. Ralph S. Palmer writes that they may weigh fourteen pounds, but I have never seen any as big as that.

When the mother brings them forth from their home den for the very first time, the youngsters weigh about half a pound. In their first spring, when about eleven months old, immature woodchucks weigh four to five pounds. Late in their second summer, when they are about seventeen months old, they are six to seven and one-half pounds.

It does not seem important but it may be interesting to know that the internal organs of the woodchuck weigh about one-tenth as much as its total weight. I found the stomach contents of several adults to weigh more than a full pound, and William J. Hamilton, Jr., recorded twenty-six ounces in the stomach of one. This animal weighed six and one-half pounds but not quite five pounds without the food, so the creature had eaten one-third of its weight.

The length of a woodchuck is measured in a straight line from the nose to the tip of the tail bone (the hairs on the end of the tail are not included). I found that the total length of adults, and of subadults,

The chuck weighs from nine to eleven pounds, rarely twelve pounds.

also, is about twenty to twenty-six inches, including the tail bone of five to six inches.

As on some other fur-bearing animals, the hair on the back and sides of the woodchuck is of two kinds. There is an underfur that is short and woolly, and through this protrude the long, coarse guard hairs. The belly is thinly haired with guard hairs and no underfur. The hair on the head and feet is short.

My place of birth was Kingston, New York, and near there, at Eosopus, the naturalist-writer John Burroughs had a cabin known as Slabsides. He told me that he had a coat made from the skins of woodchucks that he had shot. As I remember he said that eighty skins were used to make the garment. Other than this I have never heard of the pelt of the animal being used. It had no commercial value even when most furs, including rabbit, were in demand.

In spring the top of the woodchuck's head may be quite free from hair. Possibly this is caused by the position assumed by the animal in hibernation or because it uses its head for pushing earth and stones when digging its den.

Dogs and other fur bearers shed their coats each year, and the chuck is no exception. I have observed individuals molting in April, May, and June. On one August 5, I examined two immature chucks that were shedding; this is the latest date of molting in my notes. It seems that molting begins on the tail and the head at about the same time and progresses down from the head and up from the tail until the two areas meet and the molt is complete.

The animal's color may appear to be patchy while molting, because the new fur is brighter than the old faded coat. Regardless of the molt, there is considerable individual color variation. One day I saw what I believed to be a red fox on a distant hillside. Later I saw that it was an orange-red woodchuck, very similar in color to a red fox. I have also seen pink ones and some that were almost white. Very dark wood-chucks are not uncommon, and both albinism and melanism occur in the species.

When I first saw an albino woodchuck I became curious as to why this freak occurs in nature. I learned that albino animals suffer a deficiency of pigment in the skin, hair, and eyes, and this results in white hair and white skin on all parts of the body. Since there is no color present, the eyes of an albino should also be white but they are actually pink because of the blood which may be seen through the transparent tissues as it circulates through the retinal blood vessels. I also learned that an albino offspring may result from two normal parents.*

* Albinism is said to be recessive to the ordinarily dominant, or natural color of an animal. Apparently a combination of the inherited recessive character for albinism from normally colored parents is passed on to some of the young, resulting in an albino.— The Editor.

For more reasons than one the albino woodchuck is unfortunate. It has poor vision because the absence of dark pigment in the eyes admits an excessive amount of light through all parts, in addition to the pupils. This directly affects the eyesight. Its greatest problem, however, is the fact that it is conspicuous in its natural environment and, therefore, readily seen by enemies. Hunters are usually eager for unusual trophies, and to them a white woodchuck is a prize. If they miss killing it the first time, they may return to find the white one in the same den or in the same area.

Albinism is not restricted to the woodchuck. Some years ago in the Adirondack mountains I paddled my canoe to within eight feet of an albino porcupine that was feeding on pond lilies. In 1936, I saw an albino buck deer on the shore of the Hudson River north of Catskill, New York. Later I learned that this animal was shot by a hunter. Since then I have seen albino red and gray squirrels, a raccoon, a young deer, and a white crow. In the Miami Seaquarium I saw an albino porpoise which had been named Snowball.

Some animals, which are not albinos, are white at all times, and others are white only in the winter. The polar bear is one example of an animal that remains white throughout the year, and the varying hare, which is brown in summer and white in winter, is typical of animals that change colors seasonally.

Albinism is not normal, and so far as humans are concerned it has been estimated to occur in about one in ten thousand. The ratio of albino chucks has not even been guessed at, but they are less plentiful than the melano or black woodchuck. Melanism, according to authorities, is an over abundance of dark pigment in the skin and hair. It is produced by melanin, a water-insoluble dark-brown or black pigment of animal origin. The black fox and the silver fox are melanistic color phases of the red fox; the black squirrel is a melano gray squirrel.

I have noticed that black woodchucks are not conspicuous because of their color, and melanism does not affect their eyesight. Therefore,

An albino woodchuck.

the black animals have a far greater chance to survive than the conspicuous white ones.

Many animals have characteristic odors. A skunk smells like a skunk, a beaver smells like a beaver, and a woodchuck smells like a

A melano, or black, woodchuck.

woodchuck. Each of these animals has scent glands that are responsible for its particular odor. Those of the woodchuck are anal glands and there are three, each of which contains a yellow or whitish fluid. These glands are present in young and old of both sexes and generally protrude after death. William J. Hamilton, Jr. writes that probably the most important function of these glands is their use as a means of communication between woodchucks.

It has always been of interest to me to know how long animals live. Red foxes are believed to reach ten or, rarely, fifteen years, and bobcats seem to have about the same life span as foxes. No one I know has determined the length of life of the ground hog, and I have no records

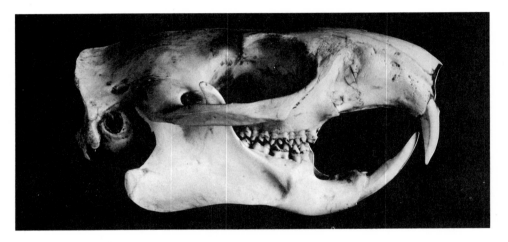

A normal woodchuck skull.

upon which to base conclusions. There seems to be a rule, however, that about five times the number of years needed to attain sexual maturity is the approximate potential length of a creature's life. If this rule is applied to humans, Man should attain the age of seventy years since it requires about fourteen years to reach sexual maturity. The woodchuck reaches maturity when about two years of age, and therefore its life span should be about ten years. Enemies, of course, may shorten this period, and it is probable that few woodchucks die of old age. Also it is generally agreed that old animals fall more easily before their enemies. With proper care in captivity, or in a zoological garden,

I expect that all animals live longer than they do in the wild.*

As with other rodents, the incisors or front gnawing teeth of the woodchuck grow continuously except during hibernation. They are kept short and in proper condition, however, by grinding against each other as the creature feeds. If, for any reason, these teeth fail to meet, the upper teeth continue to grow in a curved line, often making a complete circle and piercing the roof of the woodchuck's mouth. The lower set also grows in a more gentle curve and may reach a length exceeding two full inches.

Late one summer, Arthur Paladin, a taxidermist in Albany, New

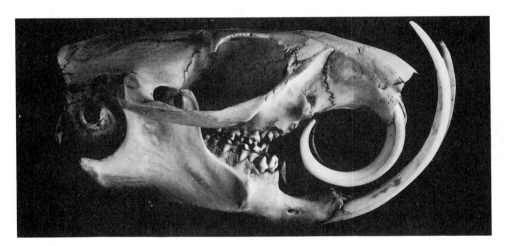

Skull with abnormal incisors.

York, showed me a freshly killed woodchuck with very badly deformed incisors. The skin covered nearly all of the deformity, and at first glance the condition might easily have been overlooked. It was difficult to understand how the animal had survived, and I was amazed to find that its body was healthy.

* The author's estimate is about right. The potential life span of an animal is best illustrated by those in captivity where they are protected from their enemies and kept in good health. In the National Zoological Park at Washington, D.C., a woodchuck lived for 9 years and 3 months, and a western marmot for 7 years and 10 months.—The Editor.

Later I saw the skull after it had been cleaned. The lower jaw on the left side had been broken, possibly by a bullet. The jaw had knit together, but the lower left incisor and the upper right gnawing tooth were gone. The upper left incisor had grown in a complete circle and had worn through the cheekbone on the right side of the animal's head in front of the eye. The condition must have been terribly painful, although not fatal.

I saw three other chucks that suffered deformities because of overgrown incisors when the teeth failed to meet. Each of these animals was alive and healthy when killed.

The woodchuck has other annoyances, too. During the summer, small flies of the genus *Pegomyia* may be seen crawling about over its face and head, and the animal seems to be always brushing them off with its forepaws. For a long time I watched chucks pawing their faces before I became aware of the cause, and then I realized that the same flies were annoying me also.

Most mammals are tormented by external parasites. Fleas, mites, and ticks are to be found on the woodchuck. I found two species of fleas on the animal, and these were identified as *Oropsylla arctomys* and *Cediopsylla simplex* by my colleague Kenyon F. Chamberlain, then Assistant New York State Entomologist. He told me that fleas lay their eggs only when on, or when closely associated with, their favorite host. The eggs are not attached in any way and fall into the litter of the nest, where they hatch. From the larval stage the cycle continues through pupa to adult.

I found both of these species of fleas on the cottontail, skunk, and gray fox. This is understandable, since all three of these animals may occupy the same den at different times. I was very much surprised, however, to find one of these species of fleas on the white-tailed deer.

Mites and ticks also infest the woodchuck. So far as I know the ticks are not injurious or annoying, but the mites may be responsible for a mangelike condition that occurs on the chuck. The extent of this mangy condition varies considerably. It is usually restricted to the head, the back near the base of the tail, and the tail itself. The affected area is usually free from hair, and the skin may be dry, cracked, and scabby. I saw one animal whose entire head was free from hair, and the scabby condition extended on the side beyond the right shoulder. This seems to be restricted to adults as I have never seen it on a young woodchuck.

The yellow-bellied marmot of the west is known to assist in spreading the deadly spotted fever by serving as host for the fever tick, *Dermacentor venustus*. Over two hundred of these ticks have been taken from a single marmot, and in captivity the animal has been known to be susceptible to this fever. However, the "eastern" woodchuck, or the *monax* group, is not known to be the carrier of any disease.

As for internal parasites, the ground hog seems to be fortunate in having fewer of them than many other animals. A relatively small number of threadworms may be found in the woodchuck's intestinal tract, and small roundworms occur less frequently in its stomach.

On cottontails, squirrels, and white-footed mice, I have found *Cuterebra,* a very large botfly larva, forms of which are commonly found on horses, cows, and sheep. However, I have never found this parasitic fly larva on the woodchuck. W. J. Hamilton, Jr. reports that, in his study of this animal, he found *Cuterebra* larvae on two out of five hundred woodchucks he examined. This number is hardly worthy of notice.

Can the woodchuck climb trees? This has been a matter of considerable discussion by hunters and outdoorsmen, but naturalists have no doubt about it. Woodchucks most certainly can and do climb trees. I saw one climb a small ash tree to the crotch, which was about eight feet from the ground. It looked about for a time and then descended— head first. On another occasion I saw a chuck sitting on the top of a three-foot fence post. It became frightened and hastily climbed down head first. Because of its weight and structure I had expected the woodchuck to back down a tree like a black bear. However, every one that I saw descended head first.

My observations of climbing woodchucks include animals in trees up to fifteen feet from the ground even when they had not been chased by dogs. A number of times I have seen chucks sunning on tree limbs five or six feet from the ground, and occasionally they climb into apple trees and eat the fruit. They have a good sense of balance and seem never to be in danger of falling. Frequently they walk along wood fence rails, and I have seen them jump from one rail to another.

One of my farmer friends saw a chuck in an oak tree about forty-five feet from the ground. It had been chased there by his dog. On another occasion he surprised a woodchuck near the edge of a wood lot and attempted to run it down. The animal scrambled about twenty-five feet up into an eight-inch diameter hemlock.

I have many more notes on tree-climbing woodchucks, and there are numerous accounts in the *Journal of Mammalogy*. Be that as it may, the animal is a "ground squirrel" and not a natural climber like the red squirrel.

Sportsmen seem to enjoy arguing about what animals do and what they do not do. Some contend that woodchucks can swim while others deny it. Generally, all four-footed land animals can swim without even learning. They merely use their feet as though walking or running; when they are in the water, this motion is actually swimming. Some aquatic mammals hold their front feet backward and against their sides when swimming, but the chuck just dog-paddles along. I have seen many woodchucks swim, across narrow streams and from shore to shore of creeks that were more than thirty feet wide. At times the animal swims with its body deep in the water and only the head showing above the surface. But when rushing, as though to escape, its head and shoulders are out of the water. When it first enters the water, its tail usually remains above the surface until it is thoroughly wet.

Pound for pound, many fur-bearing animals are relatively much stronger than Man, and the woodchuck, with its short, sturdy legs and robust body, is one of them. I once saw a chuck that weighed about seven pounds unearth and move a large rock four feet from the den that it was digging. On my scales this stone weighed a little over fifteen pounds. With the same proportionate strength, a 200-pound man could push a 430-pound boulder.

A male chuck held in a steel trap by a front foot dragged a fence rail and two fox traps a distance of 105 feet. The drag weighed exactly nine pounds, while the animal weighed only five and three-quarter pounds. However, this was an act of desperation, while the moving of the large stone was not.

Man, as well as a great many of the other animals, has the senses of sight, hearing, smell, touch and taste, but some of these senses appear to be far less keen than those of wild animals. It seems that the senses are developed according to their needs; when those needs cease to exist

Woodchuck climbing a fence.

The World of the Woodchuck

the senses become less acute. Man, more dependent on his intellect for survival, may have lost some of the keenness of his senses through disuse. Not so with other animals, however; sight, hearing, and smell are still all-important.

Animals that have sharp hearing usually have very large ears. The white-tailed deer, for example, has big, cup-shaped ears that swivel as they are turned toward the direction of the sound. The deer, a forest dweller, is most dependent upon hearing and smell, because in the woodlands its sight is limited to rather close range.

The antelope, which lives in wide, open country, has marvelous eyesight, so that it can detect the approach of a foe at a great distance, but its hearing seems to be less acute. Some birds seem to have telescopic eyes, and a hawk soaring high in the sky can see a mouse moving about on the ground far below.

The chuck, once a full-time creature of the forest, has an excellent

The pronghorn lives in open country and has superior eyesight.

sense of hearing and smell. Its eyesight too, is very good. On one occasion a woodchuck saw me crawling toward it at a distance of about four hundred yards. Many times when I have stood on a knoll or in an open field I have observed chucks with my field glasses at distances of seven or eight hundred yards. Usually these woodchucks have also seen me, but because of the distance most of them continued to feed, glancing at me only occasionally. In areas where they were hunted a great deal, however, the chucks were very wary and ran to their dens at the first sight of me.

I honestly do not know which has better vision, Man or chuck. But even if Man can see as well as the woodchuck, he certainly cannot match its acuteness of hearing. Its ears are so sharp that it may become alarmed at very faint sounds. One animal that I was stalking did not see or smell me, but when I cracked a small twig at the distance of two hundred yards it scurried into its den.

One incident that I saw seems to be outstanding. A mother woodchuck heard an automobile coming long before I did and also sooner than another chuck that was much closer to the car. Her hearing may not have been any better than the other woodchuck's but she was certainly more alert, probably because of her concern for her offspring.

Hunters often drive along country roads and, when they see a chuck, stop the car and shoot at the animal. The woodchucks, however, learn to recognize sounds that mean danger. In places where this type of hunting is done, the animals usually run to their dens when they hear an approaching automobile. They may remain at the mouth of the burrow and watch the car, or they may disappear inside. If the car stops they remain hidden, but if it passes they come out again.

Once I was studying the woodchucks on a large tract of land that was posted against hunting. Here the animals did not become alarmed by the sound of gunshots. I fired five shots from a 38-caliber revolver, and three chucks, none of them more than a hundred yards away, continued to feed undisturbed. In another area, however, where the

The red-tailed hawk has telescopic eyes.

animals had been hunted a great deal, I fired one shot into the air and five woodchucks raced to their dens. Two of these animals were in a field about four hundred yards away.

While studying and photographing these creatures, I had most success when a strong breeze blew from the chucks toward me. On calm days a slight movement of my foot in the grass or dry stubble would alarm them; a strong breeze, however, blew all of the sounds that I made away from the woodchucks and rustled leaves and grasses, so that any slight noise I made mingled with the natural sounds.

Most mammals seem to have an uncanny sense of smell, much of which civilized Man may have lost. A hound trails a rabbit and a white-tailed buck follows a doe by a scent that Man cannot detect. Likewise, the woodchuck learns of the presence of other creatures by merely taking a few whiffs of the wind. Many times its sense of smell has saved its life. Time and again I have peeked cautiously over the crest of a knoll, only to find every chuck on the hillside at its burrow, looking at me. My scent had already reached the animals and told them of my approach.

Once, when I was hidden very near a den, the mother woodchuck and her four young fed contentedly. None of the animals suspected that I was nearby until the mother moved around and behind me so that she got my scent. Immediately the family disappeared into their den and I saw them no more that day.

Usually chucks pause for some time before leaving their homes, with only the nose projecting from the den. In this way they test the breeze for the smell of any possible foe before they venture out far enough to look. A mother woodchuck is almost certain to do this. Many times, also, I have observed a chuck, returning to its burrow after a lengthy journey, smell carefully about in order to learn whether or not the den had been visited either by a friendly or a dangerous animal.

During the spring males roam about a great deal in search of mates, and at this time their sense of smell is an important aid. A few sniffs tell them if a den is occupied and also whether the occupant is a male, a female, or even a mated pair. Frequently they detect the scent of a possible mate and follow her trail as a hound follows the trail of a rabbit. It is evident that the woodchuck's sense of smell is an aid not only in detecting the presence of an enemy but also in social and domestic life.

The sounds uttered by a woodchuck vary widely and are noticeably different when the animal is angry, surprised, frightened, or curious. When it observes a possible enemy or when an unidentified object attracts its attention, it usually utters a short, sharp, shrill whistle that sounds very much like that produced by a person when the fingers are placed between the teeth. Many folk believe that the woodchuck really does put its "fingers" in its mouth in order to make this sound, but this is not so.

Often this whistle is mistaken for one made by a human. On one occasion my wife believed that I had whistled at her from the edge of a wood lot. In fact, she was so sure that she called to me, and when I did not answer she walked toward a large oak tree behind which I might have been hiding. To her surprise she found that a woodchuck had been the whistler, and it withdrew into its den under the oak when she approached.

The shrill whistle is usually followed by a sustained, tremulous whistle in a much lower key. Because it is not loud, I have heard it only when close to the animal. This might be similar to the scolding of a red or gray squirrel perched upon an overhead branch. When cornered, the woodchuck, especially the young, generally utters a low growl.

I have heard adults emit a short, loud whistle which is followed by a chattering, barking sound. This melts into a series of low notes that suggest the distant beating of the wings of a grouse. Then the animal chatters and gnashes its teeth. When suddenly surprised, chucks may produce a hoarse chattering mingled with a low, pitched whistle. Infant woodchucks utter a pleading nasal "a" which is very suggestive of the cry of a human baby. When fighting, woodchucks usually squeal, growl, and snarl.

According to Seton, Dr. Albert Kellogg wrote in 1872, "For the last 40 years the fact of the common Maryland Marmot or Woodchuck being able to sing like a canary bird, but in a softer, sweeter note, has been quite familiar to myself and others, who could be brought forward as witnesses." I have never heard a singing woodchuck.

The woodchuck's method of communication puzzles me. A number of times, when I have been in a blind only eight feet from woodchuck families, I have observed the young obey what seemed to me to be a silent command from the mother. Once while watching a family I noticed that the mother was suspicious and nervous. She uttered no sound, yet the young disappeared into the den and she followed. In a

A chuck scans the field before emerging from its burrow.

short time she reappeared without the youngsters, and although she fed for about thirty minutes no babies came forth. On another occasion a mother chuck lay on the mound before her den. Four young wrestled and tumbled about and at times were within a foot of my blind. Suddenly the infants rushed to the mother and stared at her intently. Then all disappeared into the den in great haste, and it was not until ten minutes later that the mother's head appeared. During this entire performance I heard no sound.

Once I saw a mother chuck leave her den and wander off. There were

45

A woodchuck burrow in late winter.

three offsprings in the den, but they did not come out. When the mother returned she wagged her tail and looked into the burrow. Although she made no sound, the youngsters immediately ran out and greeted her gladly as puppies do when their mother returns to them.

Spring

On February 2 the woodchuck is a most talked-of animal. Stories and pictures appear in magazines and newspapers; its name is spoken by many, and people look forward to learning whether or not the chuck will see its shadow. In fact, February 2 has been dedicated to the woodchuck and is known the country over as "Ground-hog Day."

It is an untrue though well-established popular belief that on this day the ground hog comes out of its den; if it sees its shadow, the animal will retire and we will have another six weeks of winter; but if the ground hog does not see its shadow it will, according to folklore, remain outside the den, and an early spring is forecast.

For centuries this popular legend has existed, and it is easy to see why some people believe it. If on February 2 the sun shines brightly and casts shadows on fields of snow, the weather is probably clear and cold and a continuation of winter seems reasonable. If, however, there are low-hanging rain clouds and little or no snow, no shadow will be cast. This is evidence of an open winter and possibly an early spring.

This notion did not originate in this country; it was brought over from Europe. When I was a child my parents and my grandparents told me it was the bear that comes forth on February 2, Candlemas Day, and prophesies future weather conditions.*

After Ground-hog Day had passed and the woodchuck is forgotten

---

* The Candlemas Day tradition is said to have been brought to America by German immigrants. In Germany, it is a bear or a badger that is the weather prophet, not a woodchuck.—The Editor.

by most people, the creature awakens. All winter it has been hibernating in its den in the ground, where it mattered little whether blizzards raged or the sun shone.

It is not until the snow begins to melt and warm springlike breezes blow that the chuck awakens from its long winter sleep and emerges. Individual ones, however, sometimes awaken and roam about at unexpected times. I saw one walking through a snow-laden forest on January 1, and a friend brought me a woodchuck that he shot one year on January 2. This animal was very thin and may have lacked the fat necessary to prolong its winter sleep.

Over a period of many years I have recorded the emergence of the woodchuck early in March, although rarely it may appear during the latter part of February. The exact date of its first appearance varies according to the locality and the weather conditions. In the southern part of the woodchuck's range, where spring advances early, the animal comes forth weeks before it appears in the North.

My home is east of Albany, New York, and in this region woodchucks appear usually during the first week in March. One year, the latter part of February was unusually warm, and woodchucks became active on the twenty-first day of the month. I saw three on this date and, two days later, three others. On March 1, even though fresh snow covered the ground, the animals appeared at dens near the edges of wood lots. In open fields, however, dens were ice-rimmed and no signs of woodchucks were to be found there. Cold weather followed, ponds froze over and then thawed and froze again. Regardless, the activities of the woodchuck continued. During separate years, in late February, I saw woodchucks that had emerged early from hibernation, but in each of these years the weather was unseasonably warm.

While the woodchucks sleep throughout the winter, their respiration is greatly retarded and their blood circulates very slowly. When they first emerge it is evident that their toenails do not grow while they sleep and neither do their teeth. However, they have drawn from the supply of fat stored in a thick layer just under their skin and in the body cavity and will deplete this supply still further during the following month. The reason for this is quite evident. When the animals first emerge snow often covers both field and forest and food is very scarce. For several weeks the chucks almost starve because there are no nutritious, green plants for them to eat. Their supply of fat becomes very much reduced, and they lose weight. For example, an adult male that was twenty-three inches long weighed eight pounds and seven ounces on March 3. Another male of the same size weighed only six pounds on March 29. From this evidence it seems reasonable to assume that an animal may lose more than two pounds in the four weeks immediately following its emergence from hibernation. When green food plants appear, however, the wooodchucks lose no more weight, and as the season advances they are able to restore the fat used during winter and early spring.

When autumn draws near, woodchucks are heaviest. Then an adult the same size as the twenty-three-inch males discussed above might weigh ten pounds and more. In fact, one twenty-three-inch individual, in late September, weighed ten pounds and two ounces while another one was exactly ten pounds.

I have found it is the males that awaken first and leave the den in search of mates. A compelling urge to perpetuate their kind sends them over snow-covered fields, across wet and soggy lowlands, and through muddy ravines. The blustering winds, snow squalls, and torrential rains that so often come at this season are no deterrents to their wanderings.

Because this is the mating season, the sex organs of the males are ready to function. The testes are large in early spring and very obvious. Each one measures an inch or more in length and about five-eights of an inch in diameter. With the skin removed, they are light blue in color and the blood vessels are prominent. The size and condition of these organs during the mating season are very different from their appearance in late summer, when they are only about one-half inch long and one-quarter of an inch in diameter. At this time they are internal, and only the baggy, wrinkled skin of the scrotum marks their former position. The sexual activities of the woodchuck are thus physically restricted to late winter and spring. This is true of some other rodents, including the gray squirrel.

After the woodchuck has reached sexual maturity, age and size have no direct bearing upon the size of testes. A twenty-four-inch male may have testes only one inch long, while those of a smaller individual may measure one and one-eighth inches. The same organs in immature males are usually less than one-half inch long and about three-eighths of an inch in diameter. They are not externally evident and dissection reveals that they are pink or cream-colored, not blue like those of adults.

Countless times I have watched male woodchucks searching for a mate. They do not wander about aimlessly but go directly from den to den. The exact location of each burrow seems to be known to them, but often they must dig their way through deep snow in order to find the hidden entrance.

Not all of the dens that a male visits are inhabited, because red foxes and hunters may have taken their toll of the occupants or they may have moved. On he goes until he finds one that is occupied. He approaches hesitatingly, his tail wagging like that of a friendly dog. At the entrance he smells about and, if the scent of a female is fresh, he enters. Often he is chased away, because females are discriminating. They seem willing to accept one animal but will reject another. The male woodchuck, however, is persistent. Back into the female's burrow he goes until he is finally accepted or she chases him so determinedly that he wanders away in search of a more amiable companion.

If it so happens that the den he inspects is occupied by a mated pair, the wandering chuck usually learns of this through his sense of smell and does not linger. On several occasions I have seen males lie in wait just inside the entrance of their burrow and rush out at the intruder, giving him a few nips before he could escape. Property rights seem to prevail, and a large, husky woodchuck will flee before the rush of a smaller animal if he has encroached upon the smaller one's domain.

A great many times I have noted that when the male finds a willing mate he usually remains in her den, and there they live together during the mating season. An old male, however, may go to the den of a female nearby, mate and remain with her for a rather short time only, then return to his own burrow. Each day, though, and often several times each day during the mating period, he visits with the female.

Monogamy, or at least only one mate each year, seems to be the rule, and only in a few instances have I observed polygamous tendencies. One male that lived alone in his own den visited two different females each day. Another male evidently decided to wander and started off. His mate seemed resentful to see him go. She followed him for about twenty feet, then stopped, sat up and watched for a time. Then she began to feed while her mate went on to visit den after den. Another large male nearby had been watching. When he was satisfied that all was well, he advanced toward the female. She returned to her den and turned to face him at the entrance. When the strange male came closer, she charged him and chased him away. Later her mate returned, and the two disappaeared into their burrow together.

I found that the pairing of the sexes is generally the end of the male's wanderings, and with very few exceptions both male and female live in mutual contentment, in the same den, from the time that they so unite early in the mating season until just before the young are born. I have never found adult woodchucks living together in the same den at any time other than during the mating period.

My observations lead me to conclude that copulation takes place within the den, and only once have I seen a pair of adults in contact. On this occasion I saw a male, wagging his tail, enter the den of a female. In a few minutes they both reappeared and the male immediately leaped upon the female, assuming a position for copulating.

52

·The female was uneasy and hurried to another den, while the male, still in position, walked on his hind legs, retaining his grasp, and followed. At the den there was a slight tussle, the male released his hold, and both animals entered the burrow.

The mating desires of the males awaken with them after hibernation, and continue for about three months. In general, males are interested longer than females even after infant chucks are in the den. This may be Nature's way of allowing for service to females that were not mated or that may not have come into heat at the proper time.

While the males are hurrying about in search of mates, the females remain in the dens where they hibernated and await courtship. Aside from obvious anatomical differences, which require very close observation, sex determination through behavior is quite possible at times. I learned that in late winter and early spring the woodchuck that persistently remains at the same den, day after day, and does not wander afar is usually a female. Later, when the chucks are paired, the more wary animal of the two is usually the female, and at this time she does not wag her tail as does the male. It is the female that is shy and demure and seeks the den when the male approaches with his tail wagging. The male does the courting; I have never seen an adult female make any advances. Just before the birth of the young, pregnant females can be identified because they are extremely wary and nervous.

When very close to them, or with the aid of field glasses, one can see the breasts of a mother woodchuck as she sits up. At this time the teats are full and heavy. Normally there are eight, two pairs near the front legs and two pairs close to the hind legs. Later, when the young are active outside of their home den, it is definitely the mother that is with the family. The father has no part in raising the young.

It became evident to me that pregnant females, just before the young are born, are not sympathetic with the desires of their mates and strongly repel them and discourage their attentions. The males, I noticed, when they find their mates uncooperative, go forth in search of

53

more willing females. Their search is usually in vain, however, because practically all females are in the same physical condition and mental state. Regardless, the males seem not to become discouraged, and almost every day that I was in the field during the latter part of April and in May I saw them hopefully continuing their search. Many times also during this same period I saw males being chased by determined mothers that were interested chiefly in the welfare of their offspring.

As the time draws near when the pregnant female will give birth to her young, she drives her mate out of the den or discourages his attention so that he leaves willingly. However, if the male is big, strong, and very persistent and refuses to be chased or discouraged, the female steals away, finds an abandoned den, or digs a new one. There she prepares her brood nest, in which she gives birth to her young under the conditions she desires.

I once watched a female gathering material for her brood nest. She was very nervous, and when she emerged from her den she sat upright for a considerable length of time in order to scan the country for enemies. She then hastily gathered dried grass and fine weeds in her mouth, ran rapidly to her den, and rushed in without hesitating. Quickly she came out and repeated the operation. Later I saw another female that had stolen away from her mate clean out an abandoned den. After she had finished she began to collect material for her brood nest. Both of these woodchucks worked at top speed, as though they had a very limited time in which to complete their task. Probably they had remained in the mating den until the very last, hoping that the males would leave.

Mother woodchucks prefer to rear their young on an open, rolling, side hill. The majority of the families that I studied were in this type of habitat. I have found some mothers, however, rearing their youngsters in dens along hedgerows and at the edges of wood lots but always adjoining an open field.

An open hillside seems to be a wise selection for a family den, because there the sun may shine unobscured all day and the soil drainage is good. Also, there is usually an abundance of fresh green food and, because there are no shrubs or trees about, the approach of an enemy is almost certain to be observed.

The mating den of the adults usually becomes the birth place and home of the young. The nest, already in the den, is used as the nursery except when the mother is forced to steal away from her mate. I have seen females remove the old nest from an abandoned burrow and then

Woodchuck brood chamber and nest.

gather fresh material as they do when making a nest in a newly dug den.

The brood chamber, which is also part of the living quarters, is in a burrow several feet underground. It is about fourteen inches high and sixteen inches wide, and in it is the brood nest of dried grass with the finest grass in the center. This nursery is similar in all respects to

55

the nest of the adults. A striking thing about these underground chambers is their relatively uniform size. Of the many that I have examined, none varied more than an inch either in height or in width.

Although the eggs are formed before the female goes into hibernation, they are not fertilized by the male until the following spring after a successful union of adults.* Early in April, when the eggs are about five-eighths of an inch in diameter, the embryos are already distinguishable. Although only one-half inch in length, the head, tail, and legs can be seen within the egg, and the feet are broad and flat with creases indicating the toes.

Just before birth, the embryos are contained in egg sacks that are two inches long and one and one-quarter inch in diameter. The mouth, nose, and toes of the unborn woodchuck are well formed, and the eyes and ears are in evidence. The claws are formed, the vibrissae ("whiskers") are present, and the head is covered with fine, short hairs.

The number of embryos carried by a female varies. Four or five is the usual number, yet I have found as few as three and as many as six. The number of embryos, however, may not agree with the number of young found in a family. Most of the families that I observed consisted of the mother and four young. However, I have seen only three youngsters and on a few occasions as many as five.

After a gestation period of about twenty-eight days, the litter is born, usually in April, although the date may vary over a period of weeks. This is true because chucks emerge from hibernation at different times, and conception may be early or late even after the pair is mated. On one April 18, a pregnant female I examined carried five embryos that

* In the female, the paired ovaries are small, flattened oval bodies. They are often scarred or have rounded projections on the surface, clearly marking the Graafian follicles that house the egg. Usually fertilization of the eggs occurs shortly after ovulation—with the woodchuck, in spring. During the period of estrus, or heat, the female is receptive to the male. The ova (eggs) are usually discharged from the ovary late in this estrum period. If fertilized, pregnancy occurs, followed by the formation and growth of the woodchuck embryos.—The Editor.

The breasts of a mother woodchuck can be seen when she sits up.

were ready for birth, while three days later I located a den and four infants about two weeks old. Two other females that I examined had fully developed embryos as late as April 30.

At birth the infant woodchuck is blind, naked, and helpless. Its head is sparsely covered with thin hair that is light in color. The vibrissae or whiskers are present, though very short. The claws, which are hardly noticeable, are longer on the front feet. The eyes are closed and the ears, which are flattened against the head, have no external openings; the skin is wrinkled. The baby measures slightly less than four inches in length and weighs about one ounce.

Like many others I am interested in the size and weight of animals, both young and old. At birth an infant black bear weighs only about one-half pound, although the mother may weigh more than two hundred pounds. A baby porcupine weighs about one full pound while its parents may be less than fifteen pounds. The newly born woodchuck, weighing one ounce, is relatively larger than the infant black bear but much smaller than the baby porcupine.

At the age of one week, the babies are about four and three-quarter inches long and weigh about two ounces. The head and back is dark with pigment; the forelegs are larger than the hind ones and only the scar of the umbilical cord remains. The body is hairless but short gray hairs appear on the forehead and snout.

When two weeks old, the infants are about six inches long and their weight has increased to three and one-half ounces. The snout is gray and the rest of the body is covered with short dark-brown hair. Now their claws are black.

In late May or early June, when they are about twenty-eight days old, their eyes open. It is doubtful that they can see at first because the eyes are covered with a thin blue film. This disappears in a day or so and the eyes are ready to function, although at this time they are not needed in the dark underground burrow. Now the young are fully haired but the hair is short. On the head and on the front and back legs it is very dark, almost black, while the rest of the body is grayish brown. Each weighs about six and one-half ounces.

About six weeks after they are born, the young are active and very eager to follow their parents out into the bright sunlight. When this time arrives, the mother chuck comes out of the burrow, tests the breezes, then scans the country carefully for any possible enemy. If satisfied that all is well, she disappears into her den and immediately emerges with her babies. At the mouth of the den they stop and look with eyes that are soft brown and full of wonder upon a world that to them is new.

The exact time for this great venture depends upon the date of their birth. Those that were born early in the season, of course, are the first

Two chucks, about six weeks old.

to appear. At any rate, their first look upon the world outside of their den must be impressive. They may see in the distance an apple orchard in full bloom or silent meadows graced with yellow, nodding dog-toothed violets. They may see the shadbush, lovely with blossoms. If they come out late in the month they may see myriads of buttercups mingled with clover blossoms, Indian paintbrush, and daisies. And nearby, in their very dooryard, they are almost sure to see tender green clover, alfalfa, and grasses. These tender plants will be their food henceforth.

When they are six weeks old they are about ten inches long and weigh about one-half pound. As with the young of many mammals, including Man, the head of the baby woodchuck is large in proportion to its body. The color is now about the same as that of the adults, and the baby

59

is fully furred. Both upper and lower incisors have pierced through the gums, and the molars are present. These teeth are important because now the young chuck will begin to eat solid food.

In the darkness of their subterranean home, the growing infants nurse from the full breasts of the mother. Once they come out of the den, however, they are encouraged and even forced by the parent to eat the succulent green plants that grow in their dooryard.

It became evident to me that all youngsters are reluctant to forsake the warm milk diet, and I watched them persistently try to nurse when the mother was at rest. During the early stages of weaning, some females may allow the young to suckle, and I have watched baby woodchucks nurse while the mother was sitting up near her den intently watching for possible danger. After a few days, however, the adult assumes a less sympathetic attitude, and though they may not like it the young are weaned. Now when they approach her, the mother pushes them away or slaps them with her forepaw. The biting and chewing teeth now present in the young apparently cause discomfort and pain to the mother when they nurse and probably add to her determination to wean them.

I greatly enjoyed watching one mother wisely accomplish the task of weaning her family. She merely went twenty or thirty feet from the burrow in order to feed. The young, not daring to follow, were forced to eat the food that was nearby. This worked very well because the chucklings do not wander far from the home den; three or four feet is the range of most, while a few of the bolder ones may dare to go as far as six or eight feet from the burrow.

It was not unusual for me to see young woodchucks go to the mother, take the food from her mouth, and eat it themselves. I believe that they did this in order to be certain that they were eating the same food as she. Young and old alike prefer clover and alfalfa to all other green foods. Time and again I have seen them grasp a blade of grass, drop it, and take up stems of clover and alfalfa instead. When eating,

At seven weeks, the head is large in proportion to the body.

the young—and the adults also, at times—take the food in one front paw or sit up and hold the morsel in both front paws, eating it almost as a boy eats a sandwich. They use their front paws freely and efficiently, but not as expertly as the raccoon. A raccoon has five toes on each front foot while the chuck has only four.

The father does not assist in caring for the young because he is not needed. In fact, he is not even tolerated and he is never allowed to enter the nursery. It is the mother's milk that provides nourishment for the infants until they turn to plant food, and because she is the one that lives with them it is the mother and not the father that is their teacher. Flesh eaters, on the other hand, must hunt for and capture their prey, and with this type of mammal the father very often assists in rearing and caring for the young. The red fox is one example of this system, and the coyote is another. Joe Van Wormer, in his book, *The World of the Coyote,* states, "Both parents participate in the youngsters' education. They teach them by example to capture ground squirrels, mice and other small prey."

The mother is ever alert and watchful for enemies.

The web-footed otter is one of the fastest and most expert swimmers of all aquatic land mammals, yet the young must be encouraged and taught to enter the water and swim. The young woodchuck, too, must be educated by the parent. How else can chucklings learn that dogs, foxes, and men are deadly enemies and that their den is the only haven of safety? Their schooling is most important and the lessons must be learned well, for their very lives depend upon it.

Early in life the young are taught to scan the landscape.

Teaching begins very soon after the baby woodchucks leave their nest and crawl beyond the entrance of the burrow. At this age they are not afraid because they know of no enemy. There are dangers, however, and the mother, knowing this only too well, is ever alert and deeply concerned for their safety. While they play and eat she may remain at the den, watching for enemies, or she may eat also but between mouthfuls search the hillsides for anything that might mean danger.

The very first thing the babies must be taught is to enter the den when danger threatens. Although different mothers may teach by various methods, the results are the same. I learned to recognize a number of individual chucks, and I found that their temperaments varied.

One very light-colored mother displayed a great deal of affection and consideration for her family, and when she schooled them she made it appear as play. First she encouraged them to follow her three or four feet from the den. Then, even though no enemy was near, she suddenly dashed into the burrow and the young scampered in after her. Instantly the family reappeared and the mother, feigning caution, sniffed the breeze, looked carefully about, and then sat up to scan the countryside. The performance was repeated again and again, until soon the young were preceding the mother into the den. They also tested the breezes, sat up, and looked about just as she did. Her method was to have the young follow her example. Each day for more than a week the patient mother continued the teaching so that the lesson was well learned.

Another, less affectionate, female obtained results by chasing her offspring into the burrow. This mother fed about twenty feet from the den while her youngsters remained quite close to the entrance. Suddenly she would race determinedly toward them, and they would tumble over each other in their haste to enter their den. The mother never went in after them and after she left the entrance to continue her feeding the small ones would reappear. The act was repeated time and again, and in this way the young were taught to find safety in their burrow.

It seems that all young animals play. The woodchuck is no exception, and every family that I studied tumbled about in the warm sunlight on the mound at the entrance to their den. They will wrestle and roll about, using both front and hind legs and teeth like a litter of puppies.

When the mother is away, the young may stay at the mouth of the den, fearing to come out.

They seldom, if ever, hurt each other, and I have never heard them utter a growl or squeal. However, young woodchucks do not play nearly so much as young dogs, because much of their time when outside of the den is used for eating and they must find their own food. Also, the approach of an enemy often interrupts their activities and may force them to remain in their den the greater part of the day. Puppies, when they no longer suckle, are fed by Man, eat quickly, have no enemies, and therefore have plenty of time to play.

I have noticed individual characteristics even in young woodchucks. Occasionally one youngster, stronger and bolder than the others, will develop into a bully and often force its brothers and sisters to remain in the den while it stays out in the sun to bask and feed. Usually, though, chucklings are very affectionate toward each other and more so toward their mother. In return, most mother woodchucks are gentle and kind and show a great deal of motherly love. Many, many times I have seen mother and young touching noses and rubbing cheeks, and it was common for me to see a family climbing all over the mother as she sprawled in front of the den. Frequently they would sit on her back, and two or even three might be perched there at the same time. The patient mother seems to be very pleased with the activities of her young and often she will bite or rather scratch one of them behind the ears with her teeth. While she is doing this the youngster stands still and seems to enjoy it.

While the mother is with them, the young are not wary because she is ever watchful for enemies. When a possible danger arises and the mother is in doubt, the family is ignored. If at this time a young one approaches her, it is impatiently repelled, for the mother knows that to mistake or to ignore a danger may mean death. She does not allow affection for her family to influence her good judgment.

As they grow older, young woodchucks become more vigilant. When their mother is not with them some may remain at the mouth of their den, fearing to come out, while others may venture only a few feet from the burrow. Individuals vary, though, and some youngsters seem to lack caution. Some are bold and courageous, while others may be very curious. The youngster that has any of these traits and remains outside of the den when a possible danger is present very seldom reaches old age. This is particularly true near towns or villages where hunters are numerous.

When the mother is a poor teacher, the woodchuck family may suffer, but very few mother woodchucks are poor teachers. The youngest mothers, concerned for the welfare of their first family, are usually the most alert and nervous. An unfortunate situation results when the mother is separated from her offspring by capture or death. This leaves the young without guidance, and the family is usually reduced in number by enemies or entirely eliminated.

Over a period of many years I have known of only one female wood-chuck that seemed to neglect her young. I never saw this mother teach or even attempt to teach her offspring anything. She very often left the home den and stayed away for as long as three hours, and during her absence the babies were left without guidance and parental protection. When they were very young, so young in fact that they should have gone only a few feet from the burrow, I saw them wandering about as far as fifty feet from their home. Later, when they had grown larger, I never knew where to find them because they often roamed about and remained at any of the unoccupied dens on the side hill. They were about three months old and still alive that year in mid-July, when I last saw them.

Summer

SUMMER FOR the woodchuck is the time of plenty. Warm rays of sunshine flood the meadows, and clover, alfalfa, and other juicy green plants are in abundance. Also this is the time when the woodchuck population is at its peak, and because of the height and density of the vegetation the animals are difficult to see.

When fields are cut, it is suddenly a different world. The protective cover is gone, and young and old alike may be seen by prowling foes. Hunters with long-range rifles and telescopic sights shoot from afar. The farm dog maneuvers and rushes in for the kill, while the red fox, a most expert hunter, stealthily stalks its prey in order to feed its cubs. It is the most perilous time of the year for the woodchuck, and sudden death may come from nearby or from the hands of a hidden rifleman several hundred yards away.

Man hunts for sport, for the joy of killing, and the dog seems to do likewise. The red fox, though, hunts for food, and when it fails it goes hungry. Dogs, in most areas, are more numerous than foxes, and because of this it is difficult to determine which is the woodchuck's greater foe. I have seen a number of chucks that had been killed by dogs, and in my experience airedales and collies are the most successful hunters. However, all combats do not end in favor of the dog. I vividly remember the first encounter that I saw. The dog was a fox terrier, and although it was small it was at least twice as heavy as the woodchuck, which was a youngster. As the dog circled and rushed, the chuck quickly turned so that its biting end always faced the terrier and the dog could do little more than keep the woodchuck at bay. The battle was short-lived because we placed a box over the chuck and led the dog away. The next time we looked, the woodchuck was gone. I was a schoolboy then, but I have never forgotten the unflinching courage of that little woodchuck.

Years later, I saw a freshly killed chuck being carried by a large collie-type dog, and the owner told me that his dog killed a great many woodchucks on the farm each year. Another collie was known to have killed twenty-five chucks one year during the two months of July and August.

Once I saw an incident that turned out to be not a tragedy but a comedy. A black dachshund had been watching a chuck from a distance, and when the woodchuck, unaware of the presence of the dog,

When protective cover is gone, woodchuck dens are easy to see.

started away from its den, the dog dashed forward and, gaining a point between the chuck and its burrow, cut off the creature's retreat. The woodchuck ran toward another den about thirty yards distant, but the pursuing dog overtook it. Savagely the chuck turned upon the dog, and the surprised animal turned and fled with the determined woodchuck in close pursuit.

Pound for pound, the plant-eating woodchuck should not be a match for the flesh-eating dog, which has fangs and sharp cutting teeth. Also, the dog is generally much heavier; collies weigh forty to sixty pounds. Although the chuck would prefer to run for its life rather than to fight for it, there are times when it has no choice. Ernest Thompson Seton comments on a newspaper story:

At Leominster, Mass. . . . there took place a fight between a bulldog of battling breed and a lone and harmless Woodchuck that somehow had strayed far from his own domain. The battle lasted "more than an hour, and attracted a great crowd in trolley cars and in automobiles, while hundreds on foot looked on.

"The bulldog was badly lacerated, and finally, bleeding and completely exhausted, limped away from the scene of battle." Afterward, *the Woodchuck was stoned to death* by two bystanders."

Noble bulldog! Noble bystanders! Thrice noble deed! Doubtless, the children of those men will be told the story of their fathers' splendid heroism, for many years to come.

This same author apparently does not consider the dog to be so great an enemy of the chuck as I do and writes that "barring man, the grim Red-fox is his chiefest foe."

Early and late, in field and woodland, Reynard pursues the fat, gray Whistler. Aiming first to take him in a match of wits, he scans the far field; and marking Weenusk basking at his earthworks door, proceeds to circumvent him by a well-known hunter plan—the very same as that by which the Coyote takes the Prairie-dog, and the Eskimo the Caribou.

One who saw it . . . has described it fully: A fat and cautious Woodchuck sits contentedly at his den door. A pair of prowling Foxes mark him from some

70

distant rise. Without a word of planning, we may believe, and yet with perfect understanding—for they have done it oft before—the bigger Fox trots openly and not too near, across the Woodchuck's view. Fat Monax waits till it is evidently time to go below.

Fox No. 2 now rushes up and hides by the hole. Fox No. 1 goes slowly on. In a few minutes, the Woodchuck peers cautiously out, sees the first Fox at a safe distance, and boldly mounts his lookout. In a flash, the second Fox is on him—a vigorous shake ends Chucky's life—and the first Fox comes back for his share of the feast.

Although I have observed and studied wild animals for a great many years, I have seen red fox hunt the woodchuck in this manner only once. The pair proceded exactly as described by Seton, and the second ran forward, crouched near the main entrance, and waited for the appearance of the woodchuck. However, the chuck peeked cautiously out of its spy hole, which was behind the fox, and, when it saw the waiting foe, uttered a shrill whistle of alarm and vanished. The ruse had failed, and through my binoculars I saw what appeared to be a look of disgust on the face of the fox.

Another time I saw a red fox sneak across a field and crouch near a woodchuck's den, ready to spring when the animal appeared. It waited motionless for fully ten minutes but ran off when a man appeared at the edge of a nearby wood lot. This system, I have found, is often employed when a fox hunts alone, and it seems to produce good results, especially when the prey is a young chuck.

I have never seen a red fox attempt to dig out a woodchuck, but Witmer Stone and William E. Cram report as follows:

In the winter when the ground is unfrozen, Foxes will even dig them out of their winter quarters and kill them in their sleep. They dig them out in warm weather as well, though I fail to see how they even manage to catch up with so accomplished a burrower in an underground race.

Last April, on a windy afternoon of bright sunlight, I saw a big dog Fox at work digging out a Woodchuck's hole on the slope of a sandy hillock at the edges of a meadow.

The World of the Woodchuck

Every few minutes he would back out of the hole, and, shaking the loose earth from his yellow fur, look intently across to the other opening of the burrow, as if expecting at any moment to see the Woodchuck try to make his escape by way of the back door.

The only digging of this sort that I witnessed was by foxes renovating woodchuck burrows that were to be used by them for breeding and living quarters. Unlike the woodchuck and badger, the red fox is not a digger, and with few exceptions every family of foxes that I observed was being reared in an enlarged woodchuck burrow. Not only does it provide a home, but woodchucks along with mice are two chief items of food for red fox babies.

The wildcat, too, is an enemy of the chuck but to a lesser degree. One May 20, on the side of Slide Mountain in the Catskills, I found

Entrance to a woodchuck den.

72

When the den becomes overcrowded, the mother puts each youngster in a separate burrow.

excrement of the wildcat which contained remains of woodchuck. Later, I also found woodchuck remains in scats of wildcat that I collected on Mount Wittenberg in the Catskills.

Stone and Cram suggest:

In the days of the uncleared forest before the white man came, woodchucks, it is safe to assume, had a much longer list of enemies than now. Bears, wolves, lynxes and panthers, undoubtedly all preyed on them as occasion afforded, and it is hardly likely that the Indian hunter felt himself demeaned by stooping to the chase of such humble quarry.

The wolf and panther are gone from much of their former domain, and I have no evidence of the black bear capturing and eating the woodchuck. Regarding the western species or hoary marmot, however, Seton writes, "The biggest enemy of the *Whistler* . . . is the grim, great Grizzly-bear."

73

Another foe of the western animal is the golden eagle, and this large bird of prey captures both the yellow-bellied marmot and the hoary marmot. The fine bird and mammal artist Allan Brooks reported in 1898, "In the summer, marmots form nine-tenths of the food of the golden eagle." This does not seem to be true in the central and eastern United States. Here the woodchuck seems to have no fear of—or interest in—either red-tailed or red-shouldered hawks, which circle about screaming, and even the soaring bald eagle does not alarm them. However, I have watched them run to their dens when a low-

The young abandon their dens and migrate.

flying marsh hawk passed over. I do not believe that any of the hawks are capable of taking adult woodchucks, but youngsters might be endangered.

Man is the super-foe of the woodchuck and the cruelest of all. He excels in brain power and he has invented many aids. Binoculars enable him to see the chuck at great distances. His long-range rifle is accurate and deadly. His steel traps may remain hidden and ready for hours or days or weeks. He uses lethal gases and fatal poisons, and he is responsible for fires and floods. He kills needlessly, often on a wholesale basis, merely for sport. What chance does the woodchuck have against him?

Three men that I knew killed 187 chucks in two days in Washington County, New York. Only six of these were given to friends who used them for food. Another man killed 276 woodchucks and was striving to establish a record of 300 for that one season.

The cruelties of the hunt are the results of misplaced shots which severely wound but do not kill. Every year thousands of woodchucks, bullet-torn and pain-racked, may escape into their dens to suffer alone until death ends their agony. I once saw a woodchuck shot through the body with a .30-06 rifle, like those used by the United States Army in World Wars I and II. This is a powerful firearm, with energy enough to kill a grizzly bear. The bullet mashed the internal organs, a handful of which lay on the ground, and a trail of blood led to the animal's burrow. The woodchuck had run ten feet and into its den after having been fatally shot. Another chuck that I found dead had been shot but not taken by the hunter. It had crawled, with three feet of its intestines strung out, until its last bit of strength was gone, and it died in a crawling position as I found it.

Another horrible incident, as told by Mr. Lewis Silsbee of Cohocton, New York, regards a chuck that had been shot through the belly with a high-speed mushroom bullet. The agonized creature ran in and out of two dens and died at the entrance to the third with ten feet of intestines dragging on the ground behind it.

75

The World of the Woodchuck

In many areas woodchuck hunting is done now from automobiles. The hunters, who are usually equipped with very accurate high-powered rifles, attached to which are micrometer sights or telescopic sights, drive slowly along back country roads. When a chuck is sighted, it is shot at from the road and often from the auto, although this method is not lawful. If the animal is too far away, it is most frequently passed up rather than stalked.

On one occasion I saw a woodchuck at the entrance of its burrow with only its head and shoulders exposed. A hunter in an automobile shot at the creature, and I saw it flinch and sink out of sight. The man, believing that he had missed, drove on, but I went to the den. There was no woodchuck in view—only one front foot that had been shot cleanly off and a few red drops of blood. In the solitude of its den this creature suffered alone, without aid or consoling sympathy, because for the wounded wild animals there are no doctors, no nurses, no hospitals, and no friends.

Often hunters, for one reason or another, lay down their guns and call it quits. The rifleman W. Dustin White writes, "With hasty aim I fired and was surprised to see the bullet pick the chuck right up out of the burrow and toss it away down the hill. I picked up what remained, the head and hide and one hind leg, at a distance of sixteen feet, actual measure from the mouth of the burrow." Later Mr. White states:

For real thrills, suppressed excitement and a genuine kick, camera shooting beats rifle shooting forty ways. . . . While making the photographs, I became so intimately acquainted with these little fellows, that I did not care to kill any more. Familiarity, in some cases, may breed contempt; but with the woodchuck the very opposite is true, and close acquaintance inspires respect.

Woodchucks, like other forms of wildlife, suffer indirectly and directly because of the automobile, which takes Man quickly into the most remote areas. Today, woodchuck land that was a long tiresome journey away fifty years ago can be reached in an hour. The automobile has also increased the number of hunters, and now week-end and after-supper hunting is done even by city dwellers because of the ease and convenience of car travel. I know a number of hunters who would not pursue the chuck if they had no automobile.

The direct effect of the auto on wildlife is evident in the dead animals strewn along our highways. Aside from frogs, toads, turtles, and snakes I have seen a great many armadillos, opossums, rabbits, squirrels, chipmunks, woodchucks, skunks, raccoons, a variety of birds, some deer and elk, and two black bears. At times cottontails are the most numerous of the dead animals on the road, while at other times skunks, raccoons, and woodchucks head the list. On one trip, in late July, I counted sixteen woodchucks, three cottontails, one skunk, and a number of small birds in a distance of 138 miles. This is not an unusual count, and it is generally agreed that highway travel is very destructive to our wildlife.*

Summer brings a change in the family life of the woodchuck. Week after week I have watched the chucklings grow steadily and wondered how they could ever squeeze into a nursery chamber that was only sixteen inches in diameter and twelve inches high. Mother woodchuck has the answer, though, and in order to relieve the overcrowded condition she merely breaks up the family and locates each youngster in a separate burrow. These have been prepared in advance; they may be unoccupied dens abandoned by other woodchucks or new ones dug for this purpose by the mother herself.

I have been fortunate in being able to observe a number of females preparing dens for their offspring. One mother, which was pinkish in color, became accustomed to my presence and seemed to accept me as part of the environment. She allowed me to sit in the open, about forty feet away, and watch her dig a new den, but her young did not share her confidence. I could see them crouched before the home den watching both mother and me. Neither these youngsters nor any others that I ob-

---

* Even the swift-footed foxes are often unable to escape a speeding automobile. I have found both the red and the gray fox killed by automobiles on North Carolina highways. --The Editor.

served ever followed the female away from the home den to watch her dig the new burrow.

The mother woodchuck splits the family, temporarily, when she leads them, one at a time, to the new homes. Once located, in its new burrow, each youngster remains there, and I never saw one follow its mother away from the new dwelling or return to the den of its birth. In their own way, mother woodchucks teach strict obedience.

Usually each youngster lives alone, but the pinkish female led three of her offspring to new and separate dens while the fourth remained with her in the home den. I have known no other mother to do this.

After moving her family, the female generally remains alone in the home den, which is not far from the burrows of her young, and she visits with each of them several times a day. When she approaches she wags her tail, as the males did during the mating season, and the babies greet her by rubbing their noses and their cheeks against hers. After a visit, which varies in length, the mother leaves, and though it is evident that the young would like to follow her they do not.

Youngsters in different families may vary noticeably in size. Usually a small litter or an early brood will be comparatively larger than the young in a large family. Also, young chucks born early in the season will be larger than those born later, because of the longer period of growth.

The separation of the family takes place usually about mid-June, although the exact time depends upon the age and size of the offspring. It serves a twofold purpose: aside from relieving the crowded conditions in the home, it forces the youngsters to care and provide for themselves so that they are prepared to lead a successful, independent existence when the parent is no longer interested in their welfare. The young may not be aware that the protective instinct of the mother has ceased to exist, because her daily visits only gradually become less regular and finally stop. By this time, the young chucks are self-reliant and experienced in living alone without the parent's assistance. Also, there seems to be a psychological change so that they are prepared mentally and physically for the next stage of their lives.

When this time arrives, the young abandon the den that was a haven of security and desert the fields of their birth to go on a great venture into territory that is new and unknown to them. It seems that the great plan of Nature tends to prevent inbreeding, for evidently some urge causes the youngsters to wander afar and to find or excavate burrows of their own in which they will spend the winter alone. This summer migration may begin about the middle of July. It is a most perilous time because fields are then cut and without cover, and the animals are easily seen and killed by hunters, dogs, and red foxes. From my place of conceal-ment I once saw a youngster go forth on its first journey. The creature crossed a gravel, farm road and stopped suddenly not ten feet from a hunter. Frightened and bewildered, it remained motionless and looked at the hunter as a .30-06 bullet, which was powerful enough to kill a grizzly bear, tore through it and brought to an end its first great venture before it was actually beyond the sight of its mother.

The new dens in which the young locate may be a great distance or only a few hundred yards from the place of their birth. Here they will probably spend the winter in a state of hibernation. Up to this time their homes have been generally in open fields, and because of this experience they are very likely to select an open field in which to live. Like the adults, young chucks prepare a nest of dried grass in a chamber dug for the purpose. The grass is collected in the animal's mouth but the process is slow and deliberate, not fast and determined as is nest con-struction by pregnant females in the spring.

I learned that there is a discernible difference in the appearance of young and old woodchucks. The young animal is slender; its belly does not bulge from either front or profile view and its tail is less bushy than the tail of an adult. Of course, it is smaller, but this difference is difficult to observe unless a youngster and an adult are very close to each other. The head of the young chuck appears to be, and is, slightly larger in proportion to its body than the head of a mature and fat adult.

Young chucks grow in length, and regardless of the amount of food consumed they do not carry as much fat as the older animals. Fat develops first in the body cavity of the young, and I have examined some in early September that had very little fat under the skin, although the body cavity was well supplied.

The size of the little ones varies in the early part of the season and also in late summer. During September and the latter part of August they are usually less than twenty-two inches long from the nose to the end of the tail bone and weigh between four and six pounds.

At the end of summer the adult chuck has reached its greatest weight.

Toward the end of their first summer, the young are more active than the adults. They seem to be busily engaged in eating throughout the entire day because they must have a supply of fat to carry them over the winter. The oldsters, of course, used a large portion of their fat while they hibernated and soon after they emerged. However, they have had several months to replenish the supply while the young were nursing. Therefore, the grown chucks were bulging before the immature animals even began their fatty growth. This accounts for the enormous appetites of the young.

Judging by their wariness, it is evident that the teaching of the mother was not in vain. Yet they are still inexperienced children, and many do not survive to reach their first birthday. Young and old alike, however, seem to know that some animals are dangerous and others are not. Generally they are not afraid of sheep or cows, and I have on occasions observed woodchucks feeding fearlessly amid a herd of dairy cows. Once when I was in my photographer's blind, some Holsteins came into the pasture. A chuck sprawled in the sun on the mound before its den while two cows ate alfalfa not more than twelve feet away.

Another time I used a flock of sheep to aid me in stalking a feeding chuck. I got to within thirty feet of the animal, but it ran into its burrow before I got a picture.

Late one afternoon a white-tailed deer and her fawn appeared in a field near the edge of a wood lot. About twenty feet away a large woodchuck sat up and looked at them. The animals did not fear each other, and the fawn approached slowly. It cupped its ears forward and seemed to be very curious. When about ten feet from the woodchuck it turned, went back to its mother, and the two deer walked off while the chuck, still sitting up, watched them go.

A man on foot alarms the woodchuck, but a man on horseback may often ride quite close. Several times I have ridden to within twenty feet of animals that watched from the mouth of their burrow as I rode past. A man on a tractor is often regarded in the same way. I have observed woodchucks leave their den and feed when the tractor was at the far end of the field, but they returned to their homes when the machine approached.

One time in early April a flock of Canada geese dropped down in a field where two chucks lived. Both animals ran into their dens. One stuck its head out of the burrow, in order to watch the large birds, but it did not come forth. Just one goose might not have frightened the woodchucks, because I have seen cock pheasants strut quite close to feeding animals; the pheasants seemed not to notice but the chucks were evidently very curious. I have also seen crows in fields near feeding woodchucks, and each seemed to ignore the other. Once a robin ran close to a woodchuck, and the animal rushed the bird so that it was forced to fly.

Courage is an admired trait, and he who fights against impossible odds is highly praised. There is no doubt that the woodchuck is courageous, but it is wise enough to practice being a living coward rather than a dead hero. When danger threatens, it runs and avoids a fight by slipping quietly into its den. Seton quotes the following by Hervey Lovell: "'Backed into his den, he is no mean antagonist for any Dog. Many hounds are afraid to close in to death-grips with an old Chuck.'" Another writer Ernest G. Holt, states that a woodchuck was chased into a brier patch by dogs and the animal licked the dogs. Seton also quotes the following by George P. Dernier:

"The Woodchuck is often called a timid animal, yet he proves a vicious foe for any Dog that happens to corner him. He will fight until exhausted, then lie quiet; and I often believe that this is part of his game, as one will notice that he keeps a constant watch on the Dog who is waiting for another move from his victim; and when he renews the fight, he seems to have more vigour and courage than ever; the Dog is not always the victor."

Seton also quotes John Bachman as writing,

"Whilst hunting one day (said a good friend of ours, when we were last in Canada), I came across a Woodchuck . . . with a litter. . . . I leaped from my

Horse, feeling confident that I could capture at least one or two of them, but I was mistaken; for the dam, which seemed to anticipate my evil designs, ran around and round . . . her young 'Chucks' urging them toward a hole beneath a rock, with so much quickness, energy I may call it, that ere I could lay hands on even one of her progeny, she had them all in the hole, into which she then pitched herself, and left me gazing in front of her well-secured retreat, thus baffling all my exertions!"

Seton also reports:

Another evidence of Woodchuck devotion is supplied by E. W. Reynolds, of Winsted, Conn. An old Woodchuck had her den near the house, and was much persecuted on account of depredations on the garden. Finally, she decided to move. She was seen and fired at; the rifle ball wounded her. Then it was clear that she carried a young one the size of a Rat. In spite of her wound, she carried her little one off 150 yards to a place of safety.

So far as I know no one has ever accused the woodchuck of being a coward, and writers have consistently proclaimed its courage. Hamilton praised it by stating that,

his courage is all there is to be desired. I have caught several in the open fields that, when run down, have turned and attempted to attack. Mr. Edward Drake, who once shot a young individual, had the animal run directly at him, chatter its teeth, and drop dead at his feet. They are frequently more than a match for a larger dog, and will soundly trounce a terrier much heavier than. themselves.

Seton, in his sympathetic and understanding way, adds words of glory, noting that, "the Woodchuck, though wisely ready ever to retreat if possible, will *never surrender*. No, he is a fighter, and fight he will, with the courage of a hero. . . .

"Not one of us guilty ones who have hounded brave Monax to his death in many bygone times, can say that he ever turned tail, cried quits, or died except as a hero dies."

After the young are born and the mating urge has subsided, the males are as carefree as bachelors, and by midsummer the females are also free from domestic responsibilities. It is a time of sunshine, and the animals can eat, sleep, and rest whenever they please. Unlike Man, they are not governed by a morning alarm and a noonday whistle to designate breakfast and lunch time. Once it was my belief that woodchucks were active only in the early morning and again in late afternoon. During my study, however, I found that in the summer I could see them at all times of the day. In the morning they were active and feeding, but usually only after the sun was up. This was their breakfast. I also saw them in the morning, after feeding time, sprawled on the mounds before their dens in the bright sunlight. During the middle of the day and in the afternoon the animals did the same things—they ate and basked in the sun. However, when the shadows grew long and the rays of the sun did not show on the mounds before their dens, I observed that the woodchucks that were out were actively feeding. Most of these were young animals. In general, though, the times of greatest activity are in the early morning and late afternoon.

A chuck sunning on the mound at the entrance to its den.

The woodchuck is a sun lover, and every day during the summer that the sun shines it is either eating, sleeping in its den, or basking in the warm sunlight. It may sprawl on the mound before its den, on a large rock or stump, on a stone wall or a rock pile, and even on the low branch of a tree. Frequently it lies prone, stretches out both front and back legs, and flattens its body so that more surface is exposed to the warm rays. Like humans, it may drowse while taking a sun bath, and once I sneaked to about fifteen feet of a large animal that was fast asleep on a huge rock. I threw a stone that struck just under the sleeper, and the creature seemed to explode from the boulder. In one leap it was at the doorway to its home, and in the next instant it had disappeared.

Late in the summer the adults spend a great deal of time sunning, because they are very fat and the food they eat merely supplies their daily needs. Not so with the younger chucks; they must devote many daylight hours to eating and building up the essential winter's supply of fat.

Do not assume that woodchucks leave their burrows only on sunny days. Flesh eaters, unsuccessful in the hunt, may be forced to go for rather long periods without food, but the chuck eats daily. Because it does not store a supply of food, it must, in order to eat, come forth regardless of the weather. I have seen woodchucks afield in early spring during snow squalls and cold drizzly rains. In the summer I have observed them feeding during very heavy downpours of rain, and they seem to delight in eating directly after a storm when the vegetation is sopping wet. It is possible that they enjoy the rain water that clings to the plants, because so far as I have been able to determine woodchucks do not drink. It seems that the juices of the plants supply the needed liquid.

Although the woodchuck prefers daylight it does venture forth at night, but it is not nocturnal like the raccoon, opossum, and some of the other creatures. According to C. Hart Merriam, it is "both nocturnal and diurnal. . . ." Seton adds that, "many recent observers have discovered evidence that in warm weather the Woodchucks come out by night, especially by moonlight; and are partial to a twilight ramble."

A number of times when I was photographing animals at night I have seen woodchucks abroad. Some I observed at about 10 P.M. and others near midnight. One was in range of my spotlight at about two o'clock in the morning, and three others I saw between two-thirty and three o'clock. When driving I have seen woodchucks on the sides of main highways at all hours throughout the night. Although I stopped and investigated I was unable to learn what they were eating or licking. Possibly they were enjoying a salty taste, because rodents and other

Beavers, unlike woodchucks, live in colonies and work together.

animals like salt. The porcupine, for example, often chews ax handles that are salty from sweat. It may be, too, that the chucks were grinding down their ever-growing front gnawing teeth on the crushed stone and concrete, but this is only a guess on my part.

Others also have indisputable evidence of the woodchuck's after-dark activities. Mr. Willard Powell, of Chatham, New York, killed a woodchuck in September at 10 P.M. and another one in early October about midnight, while hunting raccoons. Mr. John Jordan shot a full-grown chuck in his bean patch at eleven o'clock at night, and on another occasion his dog treed a woodchuck at about 4 A.M. Both of these incidents occurred on his farm near Rensselaer, New York

A number of animals believed to be strictly diurnal are actually somewhat nocturnal. They are seldom seen at night, though, because of the darkness and also because few men travel about in the night-blackened forests. A number of times when camera hunting I have come upon red squirrels and gray squirrels late at night and before daylight in the morning. When I shined my light on the red squirrels in rather tall trees they would leap from branch to branch without hesitating and when they missed they grabbed a branch below. This was not true of the gray squirrels, however. When the light was shined on them they would flatten out on a limb and remain motionless. One gray squirrel in a maple sapling clung to a thin branch only ten feet from the ground and did not move while I walked around the tree and shined my light on it from all sides. In general, though, woodchucks and squirrels and other diurnal animals prefer to be active during the daytime, and their after-dark adventures are unusual and infrequent.

Some animals are said to be sociable, which in this instance means that they live in rather organized communities and do things for the common good. Beavers for example, live in colonies and are considered to be sociable animals because they unite in building dams and lodges and in cutting and storing food in the pond for use by all. In this sense woodchucks are not sociable animals, because their way of living and

Fat and well-fed, the chuck drowses in the warm sun of early autumn.

their necessities do not require united effort.

Mammals have a home range or a territory to which they confine their activities. My dog illustrated this point nicely. The yard, although there was no fence, was its territory. Many times I have seen my fifteen-pound fox terrier chase much bigger dogs out of the yard. Once the boundary was reached, however, pursuit stopped, and the only threats thereafter were in the form of barks and growls.

Bears seem to mark their territory with scratches and bites on trees. Red squirrels and gray squirrels chase intruders of their kind, and woodchucks also protect their areas against other chucks. The home range of the woodchuck varies with the seasons, and in early spring a male wandering about in search of a mate has no interest in establishing a claim. His attitude is different, however, after he and his mate are sharing the same den. Now he has a home, a feeding area, and a mate to protect from other males. His most trying time is early in the mating season, because other males are still actively searching for a spouse. Often he will lie in wait just inside the entrance of the burrow; when a male approaches, he will rush forth and chase the intruder. Seldom does he catch him, however, and it seems as though he does not want to fight but only to be left alone.

In late April, females are nursing their babies. They have no interest in mating, and whenever males approach they chase them away from the den. I saw one male warily approach a burrow that was occupied by a nursing mother. When he was near the entrance, the female rushed out and chased him for more than a hundred yards. Then she had evidently reached what she considered to be the end of her territory, and the chase ended. When the female stopped the male stopped also, but he did not go back. Females are just as hostile later in the season. I once saw a mother and three young feeding before their den. An adult male approached, his tail wagging in a friendly gesture. The mother crouched low, and when the male came near she charged. The intruder fled but the mother woodchuck caught him, and the two rolled over in furious battle, uttering growls, snarls, and squeals. The male ran as soon as he got on his feet and the female chased after him, but only for a short distance. She had accomplished her task.

I made particular note of the fact that, of all of the chucks I saw being chased for trespassing, none turned to fight the pursuer, although

Sub-adults, though sexually immature, may live together in the same den. These are about one year old.

the pursuer was sometimes the smaller animal. I noted, too, that the trespassers were always males and that the trespassing was done during the mating and breeding season when sex desires are strong.

Later in the summer, after the mating season, woodchucks are quite tolerant. Near Cambridge, New York, I saw six adults and one young animal feeding contentedly in the same large field. Each one was near its own den and scurried in when a hunter appeared. Here the feeding areas could have overlapped, although I had no evidence that this was so.

Most animals fight among themselves and usually for the same reasons. Buck deer have lasting battles during the rutting season in order to win or to retain possession of the doe, and bull moose do likewise. The woodchuck is no exception, and any of the following reasons may result in a fight: rival males meeting during the mating season; males keeping secure their dens and mates; females repelling the advances of strange males; females chasing desirous males after the young have been born; and individuals protecting their home range. Apparently these creatures have some sense of right and wrong, and the chuck that is in the right usually has little difficulty in repelling the second woodchuck, regardless of any difference in size. Since the one attacked ordinarily flees, fights seldom result unless the pursuer overtakes the pursued. I have never seen a serious, bloody fight between two woodchucks, and when a fight does occur the animals roll and tumble about, snarling, squealing, and growling, until the beaten chuck has the opportunity to run away. The loser thinks not of dignity and the victor thinks not of glory. Thus ends the fight.

Living is a serious matter with the woodchuck, and I have never seen two adults at play. The very young, however, when they are still with their mothers, wrestle and play near the den while the parent keeps a sharp lookout for enemies. The following spring and summer the young, although still sexually immature, normally pair up and live together in the same den. They are now about one year old but they continue to play as they did when under the mother's care. All of those that I saw at play remained in or very near the entrance of the den, and in every instance it was the female that was actually in the mouth of the burrow. The male on the outside continually wagged his tail but the female did not. I believe that they play in this way so that they may rush into their homes quickly should an enemy approach. When playing they could become too engrossed to notice the approach of a foe, and it would be rather easy for one to stalk close and rush forth upon them if they were far from their burrow.

The following observation illustrates how these chucks play. One year on April 10 I saw two subadults living together in a den near Melrose, New York. I watched them feed for some time, then the female went to the entrance of the burrow and the young male followed. The pair touched noses, rubbed their cheeks together, and began to play. The male bit the ears and foreleg of the female, and they wrestled and rolled about, but the female was always the one nearest to or in the mouth of the den. Once they bit mouth to mouth, and it seemed as though their teeth locked. The male quickly twisted his head and threw the female over on her back. He then dragged her out of the den a short distance, but when he loosed his hold she quickly regained her feet and faced him from the entrance of the burrow. As they played, the male continually wagged and jerked his tail. The female did not.

Seton records what he calls ground-hog golf as follows:

Charles A. Gianini, of Poland, N.Y., was fortunate in being witness of a Woodchuck game, which was more truly pool than golf, since the object apparently was to hole your opponent rather than yourself. He says:

"On the morning of May 9, while returning home after an early tramp in the woods to note the new arrivals in the way of birds, a friend and I suddenly came in sight of a pair of Woodchucks at play. We had not yet come out of the edge of the woods, and the animals were at the mouth of their burrow in a large meadow some distance away. They would sit up, take hold and wrestle; and we noticed that when one was thrown, he usually landed in the hole and disappeared from sight for a second or two. We watched this performance for a considerable time, and at first thought it accidental when one Woodchuck or the other landed in the opening, but it was repeated too many times not to have been intentional. . . .

"The woodchucks were probably the young of the previous year. . . ."

To me Gianini's observations are very interesting. Time and again I have watched woodchucks at play, but I have never been led to think that the game was to throw the opponent into the hole.

Autumn

LATE IN THE SUMMER the woodchuck, well-fed and fat, drowses lazily at the mouth of its den in the warm rays of the sun. Autumn approaches; the meadow grasses wither and turn brown; the green leaves of trees become scarlet and gold, and their splendor adds to the colorful season.

Every animal must have food in order to survive; and it is almost always possible to determine the type of food that it eats from the conformation of its teeth. Flesh eaters have pointed, piercing fangs or canine teeth and sharp cutting—not grinding—premolars. Rodents, which eat plants, have gnawing front teeth (the incisors) and grinding back teeth, but no fangs.

Very often the food habits of an animal and its proximity to Man determine whether or not it may be a nuisance. Wolves, which are flesh eaters, are not wanted on cattle and sheep ranges, and rabbits and some species of mice are injurious to fruit trees. It is the woodchuck's choice of food that, in part, sets some farmers against the animal.

In general, an animal eats what is available and what it likes best. I have found that clover and alfalfa are on the woodchuck's preferred list, and it will often go from grassy hillsides to fields where its choice food is to be found. These plants, though, are only two on a long list, and practically all succulent green plants found in the wild or cultivated state afford the animal with tasty meals at one time or another.

In early spring coltsfoot and dandelion are very important food items, and to these the woodchuck adds sheep sorrel, timothy, buttercup, tear thumb, agrimony, red and black raspberries, buckwheat, plantain, wild lettuce, hawkweed, Indian paintbrush, daisy, all varieties of clover, and the leaves, bark, and fruit of the wild cherry. Less frequently the animal eats quack grass, staghorn sumac, goldenrod, thistle, wild mustard, daisy fleabane, wild carrot, winter cress, and evening primrose.

Lewis Silsbee told me that on his farm near Houghton, New York, a woodchuck took a good part of his bean crop, and once he saw a chuck in a plum tree eating the fruit. They are also partial to apples, and many times I have seen an animal sitting upright, eating an apple held in its forepaws. When it took a bite it raised the fruit to its mouth and did not lower its head. This method of eating leads me to believe that the animals sit up so that they can look about for enemies as they feed.

I have known the woodchuck to eat peas, beans, lettuce, carrots, and squash, and Stone and Cram add:

> Beans he strips of leaves, pods and everything, and he is not averse to ears of corn and young pumpkin vines; in fact, there are few things raised in an ordinary vegetable garden which he does not occasionally exhibit a taste for. He is also fond of sweet apples and fruits of various kinds, frequently making his home in the orchard for the purpose of enjoying them.

Normally the woodchuck is a vegetarian, and during my years of study I have never known it to eat other than plant life. However, Gardner Bump, formerly of the New York State Conservation Department, told me that Mr. R. A. Johnson recorded the destruction of the eggs of a ruffed grouse in Otsego County, New York. The evidence suggested that a chuck had destroyed the eggs. In another instance a nest of grouse eggs was destroyed on Connecticut Hill in Tompkins County, New York. A trap was set and a woodchuck with remains of eggshells in its stomach was caught.

Bump also told me that he had a number of woodchucks in captivity and never once did he record any of them in the act of eating eggs, although they were offered eggs and actually encouraged to eat them. Some of the skunks that he also had in captivity would not eat eggs, while others would. Apparently, egg eating is an acquired habit for some mammals, and I feel quite certain that very few woodchucks

Fields of clover and alfalfa are attractive to the chuck.

adopt it.

Hamilton writes, "Woodchucks occasionally eat insects. Two animals had fed sparingly on grasshoppers." Gianini presents the following:

We have had an unusual visitation of the large brown beetle known as the June Bug; and I had noticed, about the entrance of various burrows, excrement containing undigested parts of these beetles. At first, I was suspicious, that this represented the droppings of Skunks, but later I punctured a Woodchuck, with a 30-30 bullet, and scattered about, with blood and other matter, was a quantity of these same insects.

I have never seen a woodchuck drink. Seton writes, "So far as I know, the Woodchuck does not drink; but, like the Rabbit, satisfies his bodily need for liquid with the juices of food-plants, aided, no doubt, by their sprinkling with rain or dew." It is evidently true that the woodchuck gets liquid from the plants that it eats. The bladders of a great many of them that I examined were quite full, and all contained at least some liquid.

Two pet woodchucks held captive by Mr. Peter Finkle drank milk. He told me that they did not lap it as a dog does but that they sucked it like a pig. Very often, when a saucer of milk was given to them, one would straddle it, thereby covering the saucer so that the second chuck could not get to the milk. These animals also ate bread soaked in milk.

When eating, the woodchuck may grasp the food in one front paw and bring it to the mouth while still resting on the other three feet, or it may sit erect and take the morsel in both forepaws. Of course, it may also remain on all four feet to nibble a mouthful of grass and scan the surrounding area while it chews. There seems to be no time when the chuck can safely relax and feed contentedly without regard for danger. I have observed that when the den is on a steep side hill, the woodchuck usually feeds above the burrow so that the entrance can be reached quickly, because it can run faster down hill.

During the warm, lazy summer, food is abundant and a chuck may eat more than one third of its total weight in one single day. If a 180-pound man were to do this he would consume sixty pounds of food in about twelve hours. Hamilton, reporting on the weight of the stomach contents of 146 animals, writes that the average was "8.6 ounces, or slightly more than half a pound. The vast majority of the animals," he says,

were shot while feeding, so this it not altogether a true index. . . . We know that an adult woodchuck's stomach is capable of holding more than a pound and a half of green matter.

Nine of the above individuals had more than a pound of matter in the stomach, while one had eaten twenty-six ounces of food. Young animals usually had more in their stomachs, proportionately, then the adults. A sub-adult male taken on April 24, 1931, had eaten thirty-five precent of its body weight. . . . Probably a pound a day in green matter is necessary to keep a woodchuck fit.

Most of the woodchucks that we see are in the open, in fields and meadows, because there the cover is sparse and not concealing. But they are not restricted to this type of habitat. Woodchucks once lived only in

The ideal woodchuck habitat provides food, shelter, and sunshine.

the forest because there was nowhere else to live. My friend David Cook, who is a professional forester, told me that, in the days of Columbus, unbroken forests stretched east and west and in some parts of North America a squirrel could travel across our country from the Atlantic to the Pacific oceans through the treetops without ever putting its feet on the ground.

At that time the chuck was forced to be a forest dweller, and it was only after the white man cleared the land that open areas were available.

The World of the Woodchuck

At the present time the densest woodchuck population is where the land is open and where rolling fields and meadows abound. I believe that the reason for this is the food supply and the sunshine. Plants as well as animals respond to the sun, and in open sunlit fields there is more variety and a greater abundance of fresh green plants for the chuck to eat. Here also the animal can bask in the warm sunshine and more easily detect the approach of a foe.

One September near Schaghticoke, New York, I saw eighteen woodchucks in an eight-acre field of alfalfa and clover. In a much larger adjoining field where the food—quack grass, ragweed, aster, hawkweed, goldenrod, and milkweed—was not so choice, I saw only one.

The chuck may have its den in the very center of an open area, but more often it is located along the edges of fields, where they are bordered by wood lots, fences, hedgerows, or stone walls. When the meadows are stony, woodchuck dens will often be found under large rocks or boulders. If clumps of sumac or briers are present, the chuck may dig its den in or at the edge of them. Woodchucks also dig burrows at the base of large trees where they are protected by the roots.

Orchards, in which crops of green plants are grown, are very attractive to the woodchuck. An orchard near Kinderhook, New York, in which a fine crop of red clover grew afforded homes for a number of chucks, and nearly every dead apple-tree stump had a woodchuck burrow under it. Many of the living trees also had dens at their base. Here the chucks had both food and concealment and they were seldom molested. Orchards in which the ground is kept bare of grasses and weeds are very unlikely places to find woodchucks.

Old cemeteries, long deserted and heavily overgrown with a mass of vegetation and a few clumps of trees or briers, are often occupied by the woodchuck. Usually such cemeteries are on a knoll or hilltop, and this is very much to the liking of the chuck.

Recently a very favorable type of habitat has been made available along our new thruways and superhighways. Here, there is lush grass for food and protection from riflemen because hunting, and even stopping an auto, is prohibited. The animals become accustomed to speeding cars, and they may be easily seen by passing motorists. Along the Taconic Parkway, east of the Hudson River in New York State, I counted thirty-eight woodchucks in a thirty-two mile stretch of road. I have never seen a dead woodchuck on this highway, although I have seen several deer that had been struck by cars.

Chucks often burrow beneath trees so that roots protect the den.

In forests, dens are seen more often than the woodchuck itself, because the animal is not easily observed in the woods and a quiet approach is difficult. North of Rensselaer, New York, there used to be miles of unbroken second growth and very young forests. Here the ground cover included varieties of violets, wintergreen, wild strawberries, hepatica, bloodroot, and other typical plants. These were not choice foods, yet I found the woodchuck living there. Most of the burrows in the area that were being used by skunks and raccoons had been dug by chucks. The woodchuck may hibernate in more mature forests, where large trees predominate, but the animal does not favor this type of forest for permanent residence.

In the final analysis, all animals depend upon plants: Those that are not vegetarians prey upon plant-eating animals. In turn, plants depend upon animals. The gray squirrel is a tree planter because it buries nuts that take root and grow. In their droppings birds and mammals scatter seeds, and some of the insects are important in the process of pollination.

All animals normally live within the boundaries of an area which, in a broad sense, is their home. The home range of the individual woodchuck is dependent upon season, sex, age, food, and enemies. An adult male in the spring may journey far in search of a mate. Although he may find his choice quickly, he may have to wander for days and cover a great amount of territory before finding the object of his search. I once followed a large male about five hundred yards through a gully. The creature examined each of the hillside dens for a mate, and when I left he was still searching.

The range of the adult female is not so extensive, because in the spring she remains at her den and awaits the advances of the males. Very seldom, if ever, does she go forth in search of a mate. Later in the season her young bind her to the home den, and she leaves the burrow only to look for food. Even then, she does not travel a great distance. When the young are old enough to eat solid food and the home den is crowded, the family is separated and the home range of the mother expands. Each day she visits her babies in their separate dens, but the entire family area seldom exceeds a 150-yard square, and usually it is much smaller.

The yearlings vary in their wanderings. Sometimes they journey from the den in which they spent the winter, and sometimes they do not. In the spring and early summer, young chucks of opposite sexes may be found living together in the same burrow. This usually means that one of the two youngsters journeyed from its winter den. From my observations and from the wandering young that I examined, I can justly conclude it is the young males must go forth.

Many of these year-old animals do not yield to the wanderlust. They may be found during the spring and summer living singly in the same den in which they spent the previous autumn and winter.

During the summer, after the active mating and breeding season is over, food and their own safety are the chief concern of adults and young alike, so that the distance they venture from the entrance of their home is determined by the availability of the food supply. Woodchucks living in a field of clover, alfalfa, or other desirable foods do not have to go far from their dens to satisfy their hunger, while others living in an area where food is not so plentiful are forced to extend their home range in order to feed.

The life of the woodchuck very often depends upon reaching its den quickly. Ordinarily, the chuck does not feel safe in being too far from its haven of security, not even for food; the home range does not often extend beyond fifty yards in any one direction, and usually it is much less. When the animal lives where enemies, especially hunters, are plentiful, it becomes very wary, and the home range is not so large as that of individuals living where foes are few or altogether absent.

Seton writes, "The home range of the individual is very limited in one sense. The tracks and the destruction around the doorway of a Woodchuck's den show that ordinarily it does not go more than 100 yards from home." He then quotes John Burroughs as follows: "'I find that Woodchucks are not the rovers that some think they are. I captured one this year in the same place where I have been laying for him for three years. It was very dark old male.'"

The World of the Woodchuck

Many animals make trails or runways that they habitually follow when going from place to place. I have seen the deeply worn pathways made by bears and the less conspicuous runways of the white-tailed deer. These trails have aided me in obtaining photographs of both of these animals.

Woodchucks also travel from den to den over trails that are often well worn and quite prominent. These pathways frequently form a network that covers an entire hillside, and very often they lead to other

Main entrance to a woodchuck den shows mound of earth, the result of excavation.

A woodchuck trail.

meadows. The trails vary in width, usually from four to six inches, and they may be short or long, leading across open fields, through brier patches, along hedges, over hilltops, and through orchards. They lead from one den to another, and I was surprised to find that actually dozens of burrows were sometimes so connected.

It was interesting for me to note that early in the spring, when snow was still on the ground, woodchucks wandered from one den to another over the same route that later in the season was marked by more or less prominent trails.

Many birds, like ducks and geese, make definite migrations from north to south each autumn and return north again in spring. It is also believed that certain mammals make annual migrations. Seton states, "The Elk makes a well-marked migration. Therefore, it has two home ranges—one for summer and one for winter."

The journeys of the woodchuck are not so well marked and the animal does not move in large groups, but it does have definite movements in and out of its den area. I do not consider males wandering about in search of mates a migration. The first movement is that of the young from the area in which they were born to a new territory where they will settle and spend their first winter. This may start about mid-July and extend to late August or September. The second movement is that of some individuals, usually adults, to a winter or hibernating den located in a sheltered situation, often in or at the edge of a forest. These burrows may be freshly dug or they may have been used before. Regardless, they are generally not occupied by the chuck until September.

The burrow of the woodchuck is all important. It is a haven of safety in the face of danger, a comfortable retreat during unpleasant weather, a hibernating quarter, a love nest in the spring, a nursery for rearing the young, and—first, last, and always—a home.

Although they vary in length, depth, in the number of entrances, and in diameter, typical dens have two openings. The main entrance is prominent and has a mound of earth before it. The other opening, the air hole, lookout, or "spy" hole, has no loose earth near it and is hardly discernible. In case of a hasty retreat, either opening may be entered. Often, the woodchuck scans the country with only the top of its head protruding from the hidden spy hole, while there is nothing at the main entrance to attract attention. Several times when I was examining the doorway I was surprised to find the occupant watching me from the lookout hole only a few yards away.

Of eleven dens that I dug out, none was exactly like any other. The longest, considering only the main burrow and not the side galleries, was twenty-four feet, while the average length of all of these was about fourteen feet. The size of the burrows is greatly influenced by the character of the soil, and in sandy loam they are generally longer than in shaly and rocky soil. Also the diameters vary because larger chucks require more room than smaller animals.

At the main entrance, the hole is larger than elsewhere so that the woodchuck, when it runs in, can turn quickly around, thrust out its head, and look for danger. About a foot from the entrance, however, the burrow narrows; some are about seven inches wide and five inches high while others are a little smaller. From the main burrow there may be short side galleries, and in each typical home there are two chambers: one is for resting and sleeping and the other is the excrement chamber or toilet.

The nest chamber may be about twenty inches to three feet below the ground surface. It is about sixteen inches wide and fourteen inches high. On three occasions I found the floor of this room to be well above

The spy hole is well covered when plant growth is high.

the bottom of the main burrow, thereby providing for dry quarters. The excrement chamber varies more in size. I have found that some woodchucks dig out and remove the contents of this chamber, while others plug the entrance with earth and dig a new one when it is needed. This place is used for one specific purpose, and nowhere else, inside or outside of the den, have I ever found waste matter.

Although they differ somewhat, all dens are basically alike. There is one main entrance, one spy hole, one excrement chamber in use, and one nest. I have found only one deviation. Near North Blenheim, N.Y.,

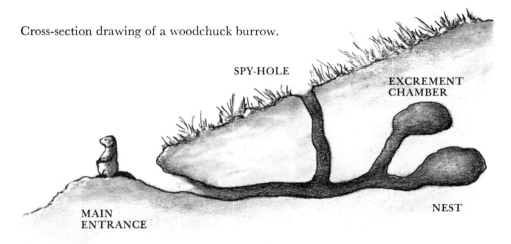

Cross-section drawing of a woodchuck burrow.

SPY-HOLE

EXCREMENT CHAMBER

NEST

MAIN ENTRANCE

I once observed a mother and four youngsters living together. The young apparently liked to dig, and there were twelve entrances arranged more or less in a circle. The underground tunnels were so interlaced that it was difficult to follow them. Measurements from the extreme entrances were twenty-nine feet one way and twenty-four feet the other. This family occupied a home area more than twenty-five feet square. Never, before or since, have I seen a similar den.

Day after day I studied the activities of woodchucks in a protected area, and after a time a few individuals tolerated my presence. Because of this I was able to watch one dig a burrow. At first it used only its

A woodchuck scratching out earth with its front feet.

The chuck frequently rests from digging to survey the area for enemies.

forepaws, alternately and at times together, with such vigor that the earth was thrown back of the creature, sometimes more than a yard. As the hole deepened, the back feet came into use, and with a scratching movement of first one foot and then the other the soil was thrown out and away from the burrow.

When some of the soil formed a small mound, the creature pushed back with both hind feet at the same time and sprawled flat. However, the amount of earth that was moved seemed to justify the effort. When it had dug beyond the entrance so that the soil could no longer be scratched out, the woodchuck loosened the earth and pushed it back with both front and hind feet. It then turned about and moved the soil out of the hole with its front feet and the top of its head. It also used its nose to root loose earth ahead and into a pile to be pushed out. In this manner, too, the chuck removed some rather large stones.

The earth that had been dug out formed the mound in front of the den; this was later used for a lookout and also as a sunning platform. The spy hole was dug from the inside, and the loose earth was taken and piled on the mound at the main entrance. No telltale soil was allowed to remain at the "blind hole," which was hidden by the plants that surrounded it. I watched this animal dig for more than an hour, and when I returned two days later the burrow was finished. The woodchuck was then collecting nesting material in its mouth.

The nest of the woodchuck, young and old, male and female, is the same. There is only one kind and it is used for sleeping, hibernating, and also as a nursery. It is made of dry grasses with the finest in the center and it is located in a chamber about sixteen inches wide and fourteen inches high. To me it is remarkable that the size of this chamber does not ordinarily vary more than one inch in any measurement. Since the adult woodchuck is longer than the nest chamber it cannot stretch out, so it sleeps in a curled-up position.

The animals that I saw at work did not seem to be in great haste, and they frequently looked about for possible foes. Hamilton writes, "The speed at which excavating is done is amazing. A woodchuck can bury itself from view in a minute, providing the soil is reasonably light and porous. Simple burrows with a single entrance, totaling five feet in length, are completed in a day."

The burrow of the woodchuck contributes to soil improvement. In digging, the animal brings subsoil to the surface, thereby exposing it to weathering action. More air gets underground, and this aids in further breaking down the subsoil so that the more valuable topsoil is formed. Water gets underground more quickly because of the burrows, and organic matter mixes with the inorganic surface of the earth.

The chuck, though, is only one of many burrowing animals that contribute to soil improvement. Mice, moles, and other small mammals have a maze of underground tunnels in fields and forests, and to these may be added the holes of earthworms and insects. However, it would require the efforts of a great many of these smaller creatures to bring to the surface the amount of soil dug by just one woodchuck.

The average length of eleven dens that I measured was about fourteen feet. The earth removed from these averaged six cubic feet, or four and eight-tenths cubic bushels per den. The longest burrow was twenty-four feet plus two short side galleries, a nest, and an excrement chamber. The amount of soil taken from this was eight cubic bushels, and it weighed 640 pounds. The average weight of the earth taken from all eleven dens was 384 pounds.

Where chucks are plentiful there are many burrows to aid in soil improvement. But what is a dense woodchuck population? I found eight animals to the acre to be extremely abundant; in very few places do they occur in this number. Four chucks to the acre is very abundant while an average of one per acre, over a large tract of land, may be considered abundant. The creature is still plentiful if there is only one chuck to every two acres of land.

Seton writes:

On May 15, 1917, when I was visiting John Burroughs at his home on the Hudson, he told me that on the 100 acres about his summer home, Woodchuck Lodge, located in the western Catskills, in the July and August of 1916, he killed 60 Woodchucks. In one month, during 1906, he killed 80 on the same farm. The dogs and neighbours killed at least 100 more that summer, so that here was a total of about 200 Woodchucks killed each summer on that same area. . . . The whole region about was similarly populated by Woodchucks. This implies 300 to the 100 acres, or 2,500 to the square mile.

The most important factor influencing the distribution of the woodchuck is environment. The creature seeks areas that afford it plenty of choice food and a soil in which it can dig its den. Since these requirements are usually met with in an open fertile field, the warm sunshine is an added and desirable attraction.

The abundance of the woodchuck, as well as the distribution, also depends on environment, because the creature locates in the type of country that is best suited to its needs. A field of a few acres of clover or alfalfa may support a dozen or more chucks while an adjoining woodland may not harbor one. Even when an area is ideal, the chuck may not be plentiful because its numbers can be drastically reduced by enemies. As we have seen, Man, with his high-powered rifle, his dog, and his poison gas, is the most deadly foe.

The population of such animals as the varying hare changes greatly; Seton writes that "the year of greatest numbers is followed by a year of plague, which sweeps them away, leaving few or no Rabbits in the land. I should say, then, that Hares were very scarce when there was but 1 to the square mile of woods, and abundant when there was 1,000. I have, nevertheless, seen as many as 10,000 to the square mile." It has been estimated that the cycles of abundance of the hare occur about every ten years.

Raymond S. Spears believes that, like the varying hare, the ranks of the woodchuck fluctuate also. He is quoted by Seton as writing, " 'Like Rabbits and Hares, Woodchucks have years when they are "everywhere," and then follow years of scarcity. Waves of animal life sweep across the foothills of the Adirondacks from time to time. . . . So with Woodchucks. For a few years, they are hardly noticeable anywhere, then some summer, when the grass is mowed the meadows are alive with them.' "

I have never been aware of any periods of either scarcity or density that were outstanding or unusual. It is true that during July and August chucks appear to be more abundant than at other times, but this is because the fields have been cut and the animals are easy to see. Also at this time the woodchuck population is high and the young are afield and active. Spears does not refer to this normal situation but to a periodic fluctuation of adults and young alike: a year when to see even one animal is difficult and then, a few years later, to find the creature in such number that they appear to be everywhere.

It is believed that the great reduction in the numbers of the varying hare is caused by disease. So far as I know, no serious plague or disease has affected the woodchuck, and this fact strongly suggests the possibility of the chuck escaping any sudden drastic reductions or periodic fluctuations.

Disease may result from unclean living conditions but the chuck is not guilty of this; its sanitary habits are commendable. Nowhere in the den will excrement be found except in the excrement chamber. This chamber, as already mentioned, is a definite place within the burrow, modified so as to be a separate room that the woodchuck uses for its toilet. The very young offer their mother a challenge, but she readily improves conditions by merely replacing the damp and soiled nesting material with clean dry grass.

It is seldom that dirt, mud, burs, or any foreign substance are found mingled with the fur or on the feet of the woodchuck. I have often seen the animal licking its paws and the fur on its body and also removing plant burs with its teeth. I have not observed one cleaning its face, but Audubon and Bachman state, "They clean their faces with their forefeet, whilst sitting up on their hind-legs, like a squirrel, and they frequently lick their fur in the manner of a cat, leaving the coat smoothed down by the tongue."

With many, the woodchuck bears a reputation that it does not deserve. Edward N. Nelson writes that the woodchuck is a sluggish and stupid animal, and Stone and Cram record the creature as being perhaps the least industrious animal in existence. In its defense, Seton says:

He is shy and modest as a hero, if let alone; he will go far out of his way to avoid a fight . . .

Second, and of larger import—for more often seen, and more often his salvation—is his sturdy common sense. Cautious is he, never brilliant; brave, but never foolhardy, never rattled, never rash; stodgy and chiefly interested in food, but careful of his health, happy in having enough, with safety and a little place in the sun.

To this I can add that the woodchuck is intelligent to a degree, affectionate, as industrious as is necessary to its welfare, brave, curious, inoffensive, playful in its youth, clean, energetic, and persistent.

It seems to be true that a creature's brain capacity is an index to the amount of intelligence possessed by it. An adult male woodchuck that weighed ten pounds had a brain capacity of fifteen cubic centimeters

If brain capacity is an index, the raccoon is more intelligent than the woodchuck.

while a gray fox and a raccoon, each weighing about ten pounds, have brains that measure approximately forty-one cubic centimeters. Varying hares have brain capacities of about eleven cubic centimeters, and the brain of a beaver is about thirty-eight cubic centimeters.

Carnivorous animals, which must capture their prey, are rated as being more intelligent than rodents, which are plant eaters. Accordingly the brain of the flesh-eating gray fox is more than twice as big as that of the woodchuck, a rodent. Yet the chuck thrives regardless of its brain capacity.

Over a period of years, I spent many hours in a blind, observing and photographing woodchucks at very close range. Because of this it seems that I developed an understanding of their behavior. Yet there were times when it was difficult to form an opinion as to whether an act was motivated by instinct or intelligent reasoning.

On one occasion the den of a mother woodchuck was located on a knoll near a country road. In the early spring when the creature was mating and at the time when she gave birth to her young, this road was wet and muddy and very few autos traveled over it. Later in the season the road dried and was scraped, and after that it was used a great deal. Consequently the activities of the family were frequently interrupted, because the animals ran into their burrow whenever an auto approached. Finally the mother led the youngsters to another den that was concealed, where they would not be disturbed by autos. I saw her lead her brood, one at a time, to the new quarters, and so far as I know none of them returned to the old home.

Another chuck that lived near North Chatham, New York, watched for enemies from behind a large rock. A farmhouse on a country road was where people, including hunters, usually appeared. This animal sat up so that only the very top of its head was above the boulder, and from there it could watch the house and the road without being seen. In my opinion these animals were induced to act by intelligent reasoning and not by instinct.

In areas where woodchucks are hunted a great deal they are difficult to approach because they have learned that the hunter, even at a distance, is a very dangerous enemy. This is evidence of their intelligence, if learning and profiting by experience is an act of intelligence.

Undoubtedly every mammal possesses at least the amount of reasoning power necessary for its survival. The woodchuck, a vegetarian, has no need for the cunning and intelligence of the red fox that must hunt for its food and outwit its prey.

Woodchucks, as well as other mammals and birds, are curious. Edward W. Nelson writes, "It has much curiosity and often sits upright on its hind feet to look about, remaining a long time as motionless as a statue." This agrees with my experience. Once, when I was erecting a blind, an interested woodchuck sat up and watched me for more than twenty minutes. During this time I chopped some sticks, cut rope, and drove stakes into the ground with my hatchet. Another time a chuck observed while I painted a picture of the landscape. After about ten minutes it withdrew into its burrow, but it came out again in about an hour and watched as I packed my equipment and walked away.

The World of the Woodchuck

Very often chucks will scurry to their dens at the first sign of danger, but once there they may stop, turn about, and endeavor to see just what frightened them. Also, an animal will dive into its burrow, turn quickly around just inside the entrance, and poke its head out to scan the countryside. Frequently they satisfy their curiosity by peering from their spy hole, where they may remain without being seen. Their concern is not restricted to humans, and I have repeatedly seen woodchucks watching cows, horses, sheep, crows, pheasants, and, on several occasions, deer.

Anyone who has been associated with domestic animals knows that their temperaments vary, and so it is with the woodchuck. I have noted different dispositions in young playing near their den and also in adults. A large female living near Nassau, New York, was the most affectionate mother that I ever observed. She never strayed far from her four babies, and during the sunlit hours the entire family played near the main entrance of their home. The mother licked and fondled the offspring and scratched them gently behind the ears with her teeth. In return the youngsters rubbed their cheeks against hers, chewed her ears, and climbed onto her back.

In contrast to this, another mother that lived in the same area never played with her young and showed them no tenderness. She fed twenty to thirty feet from the den and chased the babies back if they started toward her. Apparently her philosophy was: do not spoil the child.

The mental characteristics of adult males show up at breeding time. Some accept their fate and leave the mating den when the female urges them to do so; others demand their rights and refuse to be evacuated. When this happens the female steals away so that she may be alone to bear the pain and joy of motherhood.

I have never known of any pet woodchuck to be other than tame and friendly. My friend Phillip Hubbell caught a chuck in a box trap and kept it for a pet. It became so tame that it could be handled and was even permitted to go out of doors when it desired. When liberated it would remain near the house and always returned to its box in the kitchen. Hubbell also had another young woodchuck that his cat nursed and cared for.

Peter Finkle, of Staats Landing, New York, had two pet woodchucks. These, he said, were very playful and more interesting than his pet raccoons. They wrestled and played with each other—and with Mr. Finkle, also—for long periods of time. They were at perfect peace with the dog, and often curled up against it when they slept.

John D. Godman is quoted by Seton as writing about a pet woodchuck, " 'This individual was very tame, playful and cunning, having the freedom of the yard, and the privilege of performing all his operations unmolested. He was very fond of being handled and petted, and would play with great good humour. . . .' "

When very close to a woodchuck, or with the aid of field glasses, one may discern different expressions. When the animal seems in doubt, its ears may droop and the eyes show a look of wonder or bewilderment; it often utters a sharp shrill whistle in an attempt to startle the object at which it is looking.

Call it what you will—but I call it a smile—there is a look of pleasure on the face of a mother chuck when she approaches her young. I have also seen the same expression on a male advancing toward a female, as well as on the young when their mother approached them.

A look of fear is also discernible. Those who have seen a woodchuck cornered and fighting for its life should have noticed it because behind that mask of bravery, behind that chatter of defiance, there is fear. It shows in its eyes and in its heaving sides due to its rapid, labored breathing. A number of times I have felt the pounding of the creature's heart when I release it from a trap, and regardless of my good intentions I have usually been bitten.

It is not unreasonable to suppose that a woodchuck can smile and show other facial expressions also. The chuck has the same bones and muscles as Man, and although they differ in size and shape they function in quite the same way as those found in a human.

115

Winter

WHEN SNOW COMES, the fields and meadows, once the homes and feeding grounds of the woodchuck, are blanketed with white. Gone now are the animals that were here only a month before, and the dens, if they are not snow-covered, are the only evidence of their existence.

The chuck does not see the beauties of the winter nor do the hardships of the season frighten it, because this is hibernating time and the animal is in a torpid state very different from normal sleep. About forty years ago it was believed that seven different mammals hibernated, and Seton applied the country name "Seven-sleeper" to them: the chipmunk, skunk, raccoon, bear, woodchuck, bat, and jumping mouse.

Baby black bears are born in midwinter, so the mother must be conscious at that time. My late friend, John Slaughterback, of the Pennsylvania Game Commission, observed a black bear in its winter quarters and found it to be awake and growling but very drowsy and nonaggressive. Nick Drahos, of the New York State Conservation Department, who photographed a black bear in its winter den, verified Slaughterback's findings.

One February 12, Ray Smith was hunting snowshoe rabbits on Cross Mountain in the Catskills. His dog chased a black bear from its den and Smith killed the animal. It was a female and the hunter backtracked to her den where he found one live cub about two weeks old and a second one that his dog had killed.

We know now that although black bears sleep soundly in winter they do not actually hibernate. Neither do chipmunks, skunks, or raccoons, but they do enter into a semidormant state and remain inactive for long periods during the winter.

The true hibernators include woodchucks, ground squirrels, bats, and jumping mice. These animals are really profound hibernators; those that I observed were completely torpid and as insensitive to my touch as dead animals.

During hibernation, all of the bodily activities of the woodchuck are greatly reduced. The creature hardly breathes: in fact, it takes only one breath every six minutes, while during the warmer months, when it is awake and active, it breathes thirty or forty times during the same interval. This rate may increase to one hundred times a minute when the animal is excited or gripped by fear.

The frequency of the heartbeat is also lessened, and circulation is greatly retarded. Normally the wide-awake temperature is about 96.8 degrees Fahrenheit, but during this period of lethargy it goes down to about 38 degrees Fahrenheit. The woodchuck is not cold-blooded, however, as are those animals whose body temperature varies with that of their surroundings.

C. Hart Merriam reported that Spallanzani wrote, "You will remember about my Marmot which was so exceedingly lethargic in the severe winter of 1795; during that time I held him in carbonic gas for four hours, the thermometer marking 12°, he continued to live in this gas which is the most deadly of all . . . at least a rat and a bird that I placed with him perished in an instant."

There are a number of opinions regarding the causes of hibernation, and George E. Johnson has summarized these in an excellent way. The following extracts are from his paper:

Among the external conditions a low temperature has been considered a cause by many. . . .

Perhaps no investigator who has had a large number of animals under observation at one time would deny that animals hibernate more in a room of about 5°-10°C than in one of 20°-25°C or even of 15°-20°C. This has been the experience of the author, who recognizes, however, that cold is not the only cause. . . .

Several authors consider starvation a cause of hibernation but most of these men admit that little food is eaten before hibernation even if it is present.

Dubois . . . maintained that an excess of carbon dioxide in the blood is a cause of torpor. . . . Rasmussen found that the carbon dioxide content in the blood of the Woodchuck was increased in hibernation, especially in the latter part of this state, but decreased again in waking. . . . In two torpid Woodchucks he found no increase in amount of carbon dioxide in the blood, indicating that Dubois' "autonarcosis" theory would not account for all of hibernation.

Of internal conditions, fatness has been agreed upon as a cause by practically all who have studied it as a possible factor.

Thus, "Many authors have sought for a single cause for hibernation, but many conditions both internal and external, may influence entrance into it."

I have reason to believe that no one condition is directly responsible for the hibernation of the woodchuck but that each of a number of causes influences the state. It seems that, should one or more of these necessary conditions be lacking, the hibernation of the chuck will be incomplete or tardy.

In a popular sense, autumn includes September, October, and November, and during this time the woodchuck enters into its long winter sleep. All animals do not go into hibernation at exactly the same time, and one chuck may seek its winter quarters days or even weeks before its neighbors.

Late September or early October is the time when woodchucks normally disappear. Near Cambridge, New York, I once observed five young and one adult on September 24, but a week later I did not see a chuck in the same area. The following year I saw eight woodchucks on October 7, and a friend shot one October 16.

Those that I examined late in the season, when most animals were hibernating, were youngsters not yet fat enough to hibernate. They continued to feed in order to attain the required obesity. Generally the chucks that are seen late in the season in dens in open fields are young

It is not normal for chucks to appear during winter, but occasionally one leaves its den.

animals, because adults ordinarily seek hibernating quarters in woods or in sheltered places and not in open fields.

Merriam states, "Along the western border of the Adirondacks he usually goes into winter-quarters between the 18th and 25th of September."

A woodchuck held captive by Willard Powell of Chatham, New York, did not go into hibernation until early December, and I saw it fully alive and active on February 23. This chuck was kept in a cage, and because it was hand fed it did not get the amount of food necessary to enable it to accumulate the supply of fat it would have if it were free. Since fat is necessary for hibernating, the lack of it in this instance shortened the period of hibernation.

The winter of 1931-32 was unseasonably warm and mild with very little snow. On January 2, 1932, Frank Rudosky killed a woodchuck near Albany, New York, in the center of a field and not near a den. The creature had scraped away some snow, which was barely an inch deep, and was feeding on some green rye. The fact that this creature weighed only three and a half pounds, whereas it should have normally weighed about twice that is outstanding. Here again was an animal that did not have a sufficient supply of fat to prolong hibernation.

Seton asserts that the hibernating date "is scheduled for Sept. 30th in Connecticut, a little later in Maryland, a little earlier in Maine. . . . I have, however, a note of one seen out at Greenwich, Conn., on October 17, 1908; and W. E. Cram relates the trapping of one which was active on Nov. 1st in New Hampshire. But such are exceptional. . . ." To this I can add the following: I saw a woodchuck at Nassau, New York, October 20; Mrs. S. C. Bishop observed one at Naples, New York, October 22, and Charles Lepp caught a chuck in a trap at Old Chatham, New York, November 14.

As a rule, adult woodchucks do not hibernate in the dens in the fields where they live during the summer. In every case that I personally recorded, tracks of the first woodchucks to emerge from hibernation were in or at the edge of wood lots, in clumps of briers or sumacs, and in other protected areas.

Merriam, writing on this subject, says:

It may not be amiss to acquaint by readers with the reasons that lead me to believe that the majority of our Woodchucks desert the meadows in autumn and hibernate in burrows in the woods. There are two principal facts, either of which is sufficient, in my opinion, to establish the existence of this habit. First: as will be hereafter shown Woodchucks, in this region come out from their burrows in early spring two or three weeks before the disappearance of snow, and may easily be tracked to their holes. Now, it has been my experience (an experience covering at least fifteen years) that fully 99 percent of those that appear before the snow goes in spring, come from holes in the woods. Second: in the fall of the year I have opened a number of meadow burrows which I knew were inhabited up to a week of the time when the animals went into winter quarters in September, and almost without exception such burrows have been found to be tenantless.

My experiences agree with those of Merriam. I too have observed adult woodchucks living in field burrows in September, but when I excavated in early winter I found no hibernating animals.

Whether or not a more even temperature or a higher temperature is to be had in dens located in the woods, I do not know. When excavating dens, however, I found that the frost did not penetrate to so great a depth in the forest as it did in open fields. In exposed situations I measured frost depth of fourteen inches and more, while in rather dense pine and hardwood forests there was little frost and I was able to dig without using a pickax. It is probable that the carpet of leaves and pine needles provided insulation.

At Malden Bridge, New York, I had a number of dens under observation. One, an unused burrow, was located less than one hundred yards behind my field station in a second-growth pine and hardwood forest. On a September 15, an adult chuck moved in and remained throughout the winter. Its tracks in the snow, on March 7, were proof of the date of emergence. In this same locality and on the same date, I found no evidence of woodchucks emerging from dens in fields or in other exposed locations.

The data that I have collected permits me to conclude that the majority, if not all, of the adults hibernate in dens in sheltered areas, but the young and the subadults very often hibernate in fields. With few exceptions, the animals that I found living in meadows in late summer and early autumn were either youngsters or subadults. A pair of subadults under observation near East Schodack, New York, during the late summer and fall of 1930 remained together in the same hole in an open rolling field all winter, and I recorded one of them out for the first time on March 15, 1931.

When hibernating, woodchucks are rolled up in their nests as when sleeping. The creature usually rests on its hind feet with its back strongly arched and its nose tucked between the hind legs and feet, so that it rests partly on the top of its head. The tail is forward, some times covering or partly covering the head, and of course the eyes are tightly closed. In this position, it is like a round ball of fur. Animals also lie on one side in this same curled-up position.

Seton, quoting the Hon. Daniel Wadsworth, wrote, " 'It was inanimate, and as round as a ball, its nose being buried, as it were, in the lower part of its abdomen, and covered by its tail.' " Seton also quotes John Bachman, reporting on a pair of chucks dug out in Rensselaer County, New York, in 1814, as stating, "They were each rolled up, and looked somewhat like two misshapen balls of hair. . . ."

During hibernation, one or two woodchucks may be found in the same den at the same time. When there are two, and of different sexes, they are sure to be subadults approaching their second birthday. However, when they come forth in the spring they will be sexually mature and will almost certainly continue to live as a mated pair until the young are about to be born.

I have found one and also two chucks in hibernating dens, but I have never found more than two individuals in the same winter burrow at the same time. Seton agrees and states, "All investigators hitherto have proved that, sleeping in each winter den, there is either a solitary very young one, or a very old one, or else a pair. . . ."

Obviously, animals in the wild cannot be readily studied during hibernation, so that it is necessary to consider observations made upon captives. Regarding confined animals, George E. Johnson writes, "The waking of hibernating mammals every few days has been observed by . . . Dubois in marmots, after periods of torpor varying from a few days to three or four weeks."

A chuck hibernating, rolled up as when sleeping.

The World of the Woodchuck

K. L. Curry of Akron, Ohio, in a letter to me, wrote about his three captive woodchucks. "They were left last fall in a cage four feet wide and eight feet long with just a handful of straw thrown over them. They became helpless and appeared frozen just before Christmas. They positively did not move, except sometimes they would open their eyes, from that time until April 10. . . ." I have never known of chucks to remain in a dormant state as late as this, and it is possible that exposure to cold in an unprotected place accounts for this very late awakening.

As reported by Seton, Daniel Wadsworth writes about his hibernating tame woodchuck:

Some six weeks having passed without its appearing, or having received any food, I had it taken out of the box, and brought into the parlour. . . . It was rolled over the carpet many times, but without effecting any apparent change in its lethargic condition; and being desirous to push the experiment as far as in my power, I laid it close to the fire, and having ordered my Dog to lie down by it, placed the Woodchuck in the Dog's lap.

In about half an hour, my pet slowly unrolled itself, raised its nose from the carpet, looked around for a few minutes, and then slowly crawled away from the Dog, moving about the room as if in search of its own bed! I took it up, and had it carried downstairs, and placed again in its box, where it went to sleep, as soundly as ever, until spring made its appearance.

That season advancing, and the trees showing their leaves, the Woodchuck became as brisk and gentle as could be desired, and was frequently brought into the parlour. The succeeding winter, this animal evinced the same disposition, and never appeared to suffer by its long sleep.

Frankly I do not know whether or not the long winter sleep is continuous. Johnson states that hibernating mammals awaken occasionally, and Curry wrote that his captives would sometimes open their eyes. Wadsworth did not comment about this. It is probable, or at least possible, that captive animals do not behave normally. A cage or a box is not a hibernating den, and the quality and quantity of food given to captives is not the same as that obtainable in the out-of-doors.

How the wild, free woodchuck awakens is not known, because we do not see it until after it has emerged. Captives have been observed, though, and George E. Johnson writes:

> Two types of awakening from hibernation have been described. . . . (a) A relatively rapid awakening accompanied by trembling and shaking of the head and shoulders, following a disturbing of the animal. . . . (b) A more gradual awakening, usually without trembling or shaking, after removal without disturbance to a warm room . . . this type of awakening is probably typical of that in nature.

> Dubois states that a Marmot may wake in 3-4 hours, but requires 4-5 times as long to go into hibernation.

I believe that I have seen chucks make their first appearance after their long winter sleep, and I have noted nothing unusual. My friend Alden Merrick, however, feels that, when they first come forth, they—or at least some of them—cannot see. On two occasions, in late winter, he was within six feet of woodchucks that were at the doorways of their hibernating burrows. He moved his arms about, but the animals seemed unable to see him and just stared blankly ahead. It is possible that after months of sleeping in total darkness the eyes do not properly function when suddenly exposed to light. I once had an experience that seems to parallel this situation. For several hours, one dark night, I remained quiet near a deer run, hoping to obtain some photographs. Accidentally the flashbulb fired at a distance of about two feet from my eyes. Because of the darkness my pupils were fully dilated, and the sudden intense light from the flashbulb caused total blindness for about half an hour.

Numerous stories, some of them interesting but untrue, have been told about wild animals, including the woodchuck.

For example, the woodchuck does not place its fingers in its mouth when it whistles, although the belief that it does is quite well established.

It was once and may still be believed by some that during hibernation the woodchuck sucks its anus in order to obtain nourishment. Probably this misconception originated because of the position assumed by the chuck during hibernation.

Another false belief is that a woodchuck will never live in a den where another woodchuck has died. Time and again I have observed a woodchuck living in a burrow where I know that another chuck had died, and in some instances I have found the bones of a dead chuck that had been dug out of the den by the animal which was then occupying the burrow.

Another well-established idea is that the legs of many horses are broken when the creatures step into a woodchuck burrow and fall down. I have questioned literally hundreds of farmers, and without exception all have told me that horses' legs are frequently broken in woodchuck dens. However, none of those to whom I talked ever had a horse so injured, although some told me that their father or their grandfather knew of a man whose horse's leg had been broken in this manner.

It is possible that this belief originated in the West, where badger and prairie dog holes are numerous and men on horseback gallop in pursuit of cattle. In the East, where slow-walking farm horses work, the animals easily avoid woodchuck dens. If a horse should break through into a burrow that is not plainly visible, it does so with only one leg; although it might stumble, it will very seldom if ever fall.

A very amusing and wholly ridiculous statement was quoted by Merriam in 1886: "The woodchuck is not only a nuisance, but a bore. It burrows beneath the soil, and then chuckles to see a mowing machine, man and all, slump into one of these holes and disappear."

I have heard that woodchucks sometimes fill their cheek-pouches but this is not true because woodchucks do not have cheek-pouches.

Relation to Man and Other Animals

IN THE "GOOD OLD DAYS" the important role played by our wild life was not known. Wholesale slaughter by market hunters was accepted, and partridges, ducks, snipe, woodcocks, plovers, rails, and deer were offered for sale in New York markets as late as 1910. Before that time, hide hunters killed millions of buffaloes, and after the hunt a rank odor swept across the plains as scores of skinless carcasses rotted and dried.

Wholesale destruction was not restricted to the buffalo, however; birds and other animals also died because of irresponsible or ignorant hunting practices. The extinction of the passenger pigeon is an outstanding example; they were slaughtered by the first of the American pot hunters in numbers almost beyond comprehension. In 1869, more than eleven million passenger pigeons were shipped from one town in Michigan during a period of forty days. Another Michigan town marketed more than fifteen million of these wild pigeons in two years.

The great American ornithologist, Alexander Wilson, estimated that there were more than two billion passenger pigeons in one single flock that he observed, and there were many more of these large flocks. Today not one passenger pigeon is alive in the whole world. The last wild pigeon was killed in 1908, and the last captive died in the Cincinnati Zoo in 1914. Add to this the great auk, a seagoing diving bird, which became extinct in 1853, and the handsome Labrador duck, which disappeared completely in 1875.

Today, though, Man has some understanding of the importance of animals—to himself and to the land that supports him. And he is doing something about preserving the balance of nature through federal and state legislation and informed private facilities. For example, it is now known that many songbirds feed upon insects that are detrimental to man's welfare, so songbirds are protected by law. Also, it is realized that trees aid in flood control, and reforestation is practiced on a wide scale. It is believed that every plant and animal fits somewhere in the great plan of Nature, and the woodchuck definitely occupies an ecological niche in this scheme.

As the badger is the digger in the West, the woodchuck is the digger

Woodchuck dens provide homes for the red fox, the farmer's friend.

in the East. Very often the dens of the chucks provide homes for game and fur-bearing animals—skunks, raccoons, red foxes, and cottontail rabbits. In a den I observed near Rensselaer, New York, I recorded the original owner, the woodchuck; during the winter, when the chuck was hibernating, a cottontail rabbit made the den its emergency home.

Raccoons also live in woodchuck burrows.

Later, a skunk took possession. Some time after the skunk left, a raccoon moved in, and finally the burrow was used as a nursery for a family of red foxes. In this case, five different species of mammals used the very same den.

Of what value is this to Man? Some people want to know the dollar-and-cents value of an animal, while others want to know its value to agriculture, as a rodent destroyer, or as an insect eater. True, the woodchuck does not eat rodents or insects, but it provides homes for animals that do. The red fox and the skunk feed upon field mice, grasshoppers, beetles, and other creatures that destroy farm crops. In aiding these animals, the woodchuck indirectly helps the farmer and, in so doing, benefits all of us.

The cottontail rabbit, an important small-game animal, winters in the chuck's burrow.

The flesh of the woodchuck furnishes food for the red fox, and many fox cubs have been sustained on the tender meat of young chucks. As well as being a farmers' aid, the red fox, like the raccoon and skunk, is a valuable fur bearer, so indirectly the woodchuck befriends the trapper.

Then, by providing winter shelter for the cottontail, it puts the hunter in its debt, because the rabbit is a very important small-game animal.

Other creatures also frequent woodchuck burrows. I have seen, in snow, the tracks of pheasants leading in and out of chuck dens, and in two instances I tracked gray foxes into woodchuck burrows. One August, I saw a long-tailed weasel enter a den and learned, from tracks in the snow, that weasels frequent chuck dens in winter.

Hamilton writes:

On March 26, 1932, I set about twenty traps for woodchucks. There was a quantity of snow on the ground at this time. Five chipmunks, *Tamias striatus lysteri,* were caught in the morning, all rutting individuals. . . . Possibly they frequently resort to such chambers for their hibernating period, making little tunnels or pockets to the side of the chamber.

This does not surprise me, because rodents are not flesh eaters and therefore they do not prey upon each other. I have found muskrats living with beavers in the beaver lodge, and I have recorded the house rat occupying muskrat houses.

The woodchuck does more than provide a home for itself and other animals. As has been already discussed, the chuck aids in soil improvement by bringing subsoil to the surface. Hamilton estimates that in New York State alone "over 1,600,000 tons of earth is removed to the surface each year. This is the equivalent of 32,000 loaded carloads each of fifty tons capacity."

The woodchuck is a valuable game animal and is considered difficult sport when hunted in a fair manner. Those who hunt it are bound to respect its self-preserving qualities. Few hunters would see the woodchuck exterminated, for they realize that to a creature affording them sport and recreation they owe at least a kind thought and a generous amount of praise. Although the animal is not protected by law, the gentleman sportsman will not shoot the chuck in spring or early summer. Late July, August, and September is woodchuck-hunting time. During these months the young are big enough to be game and they are almost self-reliant, whereas in spring and early summer the killing of one adult female might mean the extermination of a whole family and a great amount of suffering for the motherless infants.

Some hunters are wasteful killers, while others eat the animals that they shoot. Unlike domestic poultry, the woodchuck feeds only upon fresh green plants and when properly cooked is very delicious. When fried, pot-roasted, or made into sour meat similar to hasenpfeffer, it is very tasty.

Another form of woodchuck hunting is bloodless, safe, and approved by all. This is camera hunting, and I know from personal experience that it is much more difficult than rifle hunting. Some of my friends are expert riflemen, and with high-powered guns, telescopic sights, and high-velocity cartridges they are able to hit a woodchuck at a distance of several hundred yards. My best photographs, though, have been made when I was only twelve to fourteen feet from the animal. Furthermore, a photo can be seen and enjoyed by many for an indefinite period of time, while the killing of a woodchuck affords only a brief moment of satisfaction for the hunter.

The wild animal photographer is a member of a large, understanding group of nature lovers, comprised of men, women, and children, who ask no more than to look upon wild life when it is free and unmolested. The position of this group could be confirmed no better than by the words of my late friend Edward A. Preble:

And to whom belongs this wild life that is so fast being sacrificed to greed and vanity, and at such serious cost to our finer qualities, however dulled? These creatures of the wild belong to all of us in so far as we have the mind and the will to appreciate their beauty and companionship. They are a part of that great and glorious heritage that has come to us who read these lines, and to the millions who will never see them, and to our children and their children. And they belong peculiarly to those of us who have not the wish to sacrifice them for our own temporary pleasure or profit. As for those who exploit them, and to whom wild life is valued only in dollars, they have long since destroyed their share.

Relation to Man and Other Animals

A report made in 1883 by the New Hampshire Legislative Woodchuck Committee illustrates the attitude of some people toward the woodchuck. In my opinion, it is a "classic." Merriam quotes this in part as follows:

Your committee finds that the woodchuck is absolutely destitute of any interesting qualities, that is, such qualities as would recommend it to the average inhabitant of New Hampshire. . . . Its body is thick and squatty, and its legs so short that its belly seems almost to touch the ground. This is not a pleasing picture. Its size varies all the way from those reared in Strafford County to the huge fellows that claim a homestead among the fertile farms of Grafton. Woodchucks have been known to attain a large size, even 15 pounds. This, however, would not be an average woodchuck. The casual observer is not attracted by the brilliancy of a woodchuck's colour. When one thinks it over, it certainly would seem that the family of woodchucks was designed and brought forth under conditions of severe simplicity. While the usual colour cannot be said to be a decided red, it is not Auburn, but more like Derry, which is next to Auburn. Your committee has now in mind the under side of the creature. The body, even in very young woodchucks, is inclined to be gray—a very significant circumstance in the mind of your committee, when the total depravity of the animal is considered. . . . Like thieves in all climes, the woodchuck remains securely concealed in its hole for a great part of the day. Its only purpose in venturing forth during the daytime is to get a good lay of the land. . . . Like the bear, the gait of the thing under consideration is plantigrade, but in order to occasionally exercise its toes it climbs small trees and shrubs, then, perfectly satisfied that its pedal extremities are in good working trim, it descends to the ground and again resumes its monotonous waddle. The woodchuck, despite its deformities both of mind and body, possesses some of the amenities of a higher civilization. It cleans its face after the manner of the squirrels, and licks its fur after the manner of a cat. Your committee is too wise, however, to be deceived by this purely superficial observance of better habits. Contemporaneous with the ark, the woodchuck has not made any material progress in social science, and it is now too late to reform the wayward sinner. The average age of the woodchuck is too long to please your committee. . . . Your committee is confident that a small bounty will prove of incalculable good; at all vents, even as an experiment, it is certainly worth trying; therefore your committee would respectfully recommend that the accompanying bill be passed.

133

A wild-animal photographer's trophy.

Following the issue of this statement, an act providing a bounty of ten cents per woodchuck was enacted.

In general, farmers in certain areas consider the chuck to be a nuisance because of what it eats. In and about fields of clover and alfalfa, woodchucks are most abundant, and to these crops most damage is done. The creatures eat and trample down some of these greens, but the damage is not nearly so extensive as some would have us believe. It is an unfortunate human trait to exaggerate loss. I have had farmers tell me that forty or sixty of their chickens were killed because of red fox or raccoon raids, when one-tenth of that number would have been high. One man said that sixty-five acres of his land was flooded by beavers when I knew, because I had taken measurements, that fewer than twenty acres were under water.

Farmers who were reasonable, intelligent, and truthful agreed with me that the destructive habits of the woodchuck have been greatly overestimated. It seems that the greatest damage is not the amount of clover and alfalfa that the creature eats or tramples down; it is not the menace of its burrows to the legs of working horses; but it is the possible dulling of the knives of farm machinery because of the mounds of earth and stone at the entrance of the dens.

In grape-growing country, I learned that the woodchuck did no harm; at least no damage was reported to me. In well-kept orchards where the ground was clean and free from vegetation, chucks were absent or very scarce and I saw no damage done to the trees. Truck gardens that I saw, suffered, however, because woodchucks are very fond of the vegetables grown there. In most, though, the creatures were easily controlled because these gardens were relatively small.

The value of the woodchuck to you depends entirely upon the group, or groups, to which you belong. But farmers, hunters, trappers, and nature lovers commonly agree that the life of the woodchuck is one of the most fascinating of all the small animals in our summer woods and open fields.

The Different Races of Woodchucks

When I was young technical names annoyed me, and not until I journeyed far from home did I understand their importance. A man I talked with in Wyoming knew the marmot but he did not know the woodchuck, and men in North Carolina did not know that their monax and the woodchuck was the same animal.

It became evident to me that any creature might have a different name in different parts of the country. Technical names, however, are constant. Regardless of locality they do not change, and an animal may be known the world over by its technical name while its common name applies only in the area in which it is used.

In the United States and Canada, there are thirty-one different races or subspecies of woodchucks. These divide naturally into three distinct groups, and each member of these groups has been given a technical name.

The *flaviventris* group includes twelve subspecies known as yellow-bellied marmots. They are western animals and may weigh up to seventeen pounds. The general color is yellowish-brown with silver-tipped guard hairs in the back and a dark head and tail. There is a whitish band on the face in front of the eyes, and the feet are tawny. Because of the tawny or yellowish feet, the animal has been called the yellow-footed marmot.

Another group, with ten members, is the species *calgata,* the hoary marmot. These are the largest animals and may weigh up to twenty pounds. They are whitish or gray with a black and white facial pattern and dark feet and tail. These animals live in the far north and in

The *monax* group is made up of nine subspecies.

Alaska, practically to the Arctic Circle.

The third group of North American woodchucks is the *monax* group, which is comprised of nine subspecies. These animals are generally brown with white-tipped hairs on the back that produce a grizzly-gray appearance. The feet and tail are nearly black. These animals weigh up to fourteen pounds, and they are the smallest of the three groups. These are the woodchucks with which we have dealt.

The following information is based upon the *List of North American Recent Mammals* by Gerrit S. Miller, Jr.

Marmota monax monax (Maryland woodchuck). Range: middle-eastern United States from Pennsylvania, New Jersey (?), Ohio, Indiana, Illinois, and Iowa south to the northern parts of South Carolina, Georgia, Alabama, and Arkansas; west to eastern Kansas.

Marmota monax rufescens (red-bellied woodchuck). Range: eastern North Dakota; central and southern Minnesota, Wisconsin, and Michigan; southern Ontario; the greater part of New York (including Long Island); the higher parts of western Massachusetts; and all of Vermont.

Marmota monax bunkeri (Kansas woodchuck). Range: Northeastern

137

Kansas south to Woodson and Greenwood counties, and west along the Kansas River and tributaries, northwestern Missouri, western Iowa, and southeastern Nebraska.

Marmota monax preblorum (New England woodchuck). Range: southern New England, from Connecticut to New Hampshire and southern Maine.

Marmota monax ignava (Labrador woodchuck). Range: known definitely only from the vicinity of Black Bay on Strait of Belle Isle in Labrador, Canada; probably north to Hamilton Inlet.

Marmota monax canadensis (Canada woodchuck). Range: the greater part of the interior of Canada, from Great Slave Lake and York

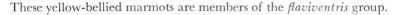

These yellow-bellied marmots are members of the *flaviventris* group.

Factory south to southern Alberta (Red Deer), central Saskatchewan (Cumberland House), northern Minnesota, northern Wisconsin, northern Michigan, central Ontario, southern Quebec, New Brunswick, Nova Scotia and northern Vermont; the northern and eastern limits of its range in Quebec are unknown.

Marmota monax johnsoni (Gaspé woodchuck). Range: Gaspé Peninsula from Percé at sea level up to about 1,500 feet in the upper branches of the Grand Cascapedia River.

Marmota monax petrensis (British Columbia woodchuck). Range: the interior ranges of southern British Columbia and adjacent parts of the United States, from Barkerville, British Columbia, south to Thompson Pass, Idaho.

Marmota monax ochracea (Alaska woodchuck). Range: the interior mountain ranges of Yukon and northern British Columbia, from Fortymile Creek south to the Babine Mountains (and Lake Stewart?).

These subspecies differ only in size and color, and the slight variations may be difficult to detect. In general, the habits of all woodchucks are very much alike. The only differences are those imposed by geographic location.

Suggested Reading References

Abbott, Jacob B., "Notes on the Common Woodchuck." *Pennsylvania Game News*, vol. 15, no. 2 (May, 1944).

Beard, Daniel C., and others, *Fading Trails*. New York, 1942.

Bowdish, B. S., "Tree-Climbing Woodchucks." *Journal of Mammalogy*, vol. 3, no. 4 (November, 1922).

Bradley, W. Z., "Woodchuck Defense." *Pennsylvania Game News,* vol. 15, no. 12 (March, 1945).

Burt, William H., *Mammals of the Great Lakes Region*. Ann Arbor, Mich., 1957.

Burton, Maurice, *Systematic Dictionary of Mammals of the World*. New York, 1962.

Cahalane, Victor H., *Mammals of North America*. New York, 1947.

Chapman, Floyd B., "Mr. Woodchuck, Master Conservationist." *Ohio Conservation Bulletin* (June, 1938).

Cockrum, E. Lendell, *Introduction to Mammalogy*. New York, 1962.

Cook, David B., "Your Neighbor the Woodchuck." *Audubon Magazine,* vol. 47, no. 4, pp. 201-206 (July-August, 1945).

Cram, William Everett, "Another Swimming Woodchuck." *Journal of Mammalogy*, vol. 4 (1923).

Ewing, Henry Ellsworth, *A Manual of External Parasites*. Baltimore, 1929.

Hamilton, William J., "The Life History of the Rufescent Woodchuck *Marmota monax rufescens* Howell." *Carnegie Museum Annals,* vol. 23 (1934).

Hamilton, William J., Jr., *The Mammals of Eastern United States*. Ithaca, N.Y., 1943.

Heinhold, George, "Weather Prophet Without Honor." *Saturday Evening Post* (January 31, 1948).

Suggested Reading References

Hickman, C. P., "Woodchucks Climb Trees." *Journal of Mammalogy,* vol. 3 (1922).

Holt, Ernest G., "Midwinter Record of Woodchuck in Western Pennsylvania." *Journal of Mammalogy,* vol. 10 (1929).

Johnson, Charles E., "Aquatic Habits of the Woodchuck." *Journal of Mammalogy,* vol. 4, no. 2 (May, 1923).

Johnson, George E., "Hibernation In Mammals." *Quarterly Review of Biology,* vol. 6 (1931).

Lyman, Charles K., and Albert R. Dawe, (eds.). "Mammalian Hibernation." *Proceedings of the First International Symposium of Natural Mammal Hibernation.* Cambridge, Mass., 1960.

Mearns, Edgar A., "Notes on the Mammals of the Catskill Mountains, New York." *Proceedings of the United States National Museum,* vol. 21 (1899).

Miller, Gerrit S., Jr., and Remington Kellogg, "List of North American Recent Mammals." Washington, Smithsonian Insitution, 1955.

Moore, Clifford B., *The Book of Wild Pets.* Newton Centre, Mass., 1954.

Nelson, Edward W., "Smaller Mammals of North America." *National Geographic Magazine,* vol. 33 (1918).

Palmer, E. Lawrence, "Holes in the Ground." *The American Weekly* (February 11, 1945).

Palmer, Ralph S., *The Mammal Guide.* Garden City, N.Y., 1954.

Phillips, John C., "A Swimming Woodchuck." *Journal of Mammalogy,* vol. 4 (1923).

Preble, Edward A., "Our Disappearing Fur Bearers." *Nature Magazine,* vol. 10 (1927).

Ripper, Charles L., *Woodchucks and Their Kin.* New York, 1963.

Sanderson, Ivan T., *Living Mammals of the World.* Garden City, N.Y., n. d.

Schoonmaker, W. J., "Notes on Some Mammals of Allegany State Park." *Journal of Mammalogy,* vol. 10 (1929).

———, "Weights of Some New York Mammals." *Journal of Mammalogy,* vol. 10 (1929).

———, "How Heavy Is Your Game?" *Field and Stream* (June, 1936).

———, "The Value of Woodchucks." *Nature Magazine,* vol. 27, no. 5 (May, 1936).

————, "The Woodchuck: Lord of the Clover Field." *New York Zoological Society Bulletin,* vol. 61, no. 1 (January-February, 1938).

————, "The Woodchuck." *Nature Magazine* (January, 1947).

————, "I Like Woodchucks." *Bulletin of the Rochester Museum of Arts and Sciences.* vol. 29, no. 2 (February, 1956).

Seton, Ernest Thompson, *Lives of Game Animals,* vol. 4. New York, 1929.

Shelford, Victor E., *Laboratory and Field Ecology.* Baltimore, 1929.

Stone, Witmer, and William Everett Cram, *American Animals.* New York, 1905.

Walker, Ernest P., and others, *Mammals of the World,* vol. 2, p. 706, Baltimore, 1964.

White, W. Dustin, "This War on Chucks." *Field and Stream* (March, 1931).

Index

143

Index